H A Z E   C A P

330°   300°   270°   240°   65°
60°

COPAIS
PALUS

UTOPIA

PROPONTIS
II

HERCULIS
PONS

PROPONTIS
I

DIOSCURIA   UMBRA

CASIUS

CEBRENIA

NILOSYRTIS

PROTONILUS   COLOE
P.

AETHERIA

ISMENIUS
LACUS

NIA

ILUS

MEROE

NEITH
REGIO

STYX   PHLEGRA   30°

EDEN

MOAB

ARABIA

AERIA

ISIDIS
REGIO

ELYSIUM

TRIVIUM
CHARONTIS

SYRTIS   MAJOR

NEPENTHES

AMENTHES

CERBERUS

MESOGAEA

EDOM

OENOTRIA

MOERIS
LACUS

AETHIOPIS

AEOLIS

0°   East

SINUS   SABAEUS

DELTOTON
SINUS

CROCEA

LIBYA

GOMER

CYCLOPUM

ZEPHYRIA

NI

ALIONIS   REGIO

IAPYGIA

MARE

SYRTIS
MINOR

HESPERIA

MARE

TRITONIS S.

SINUS

TRINACRIA

TYRRHENUM

LAESTRYGONUM
SINUS

RASENA

ANDORAE
FRETUM

MARE
SERPENTIS

HELLESPONTUS

YAONIS   REGIO

MARE

(AUSONIA
BOREALIS)

AUSONIA

CIMMERIUM   -30°

YAONIS FRETUM

HADRIACUM

(AUSONIA
AUSTRALIS)

CHIS

HELLAS

ZEA
LACUS

ERIDANIA

SCAMANDER

ELECTRIS

CHERSONESUS

TIPHYS
FRETUM

DEPRESSIO

SINUS

MARE   -60°

HELLESPONTICA

PROMETHEI

CHRONIUM

L E

THYLE II

-65°

330°   300°   270°   240°   210°   180°

THE NEW MARS

The Martian map forming the front endpaper is an example of one of the best representations of the surface of Mars shortly before the Mariner 9 mission. It shows the dark and light markings due to regions of different albedo, or reflectivity. These regions have long been visible from Earth. The classical names given by 19th- and 20th-century astronomers are shown on the map. The map shows no geologic structure because none could be detected from Earth.

The Martian map forming the rear endpaper is the product of the Mariner 9 mission and shows the abundant, varied geologic structures of the planet, including craters, volcanoes, and riverlike channels. Selected examples illustrate the names assigned to these structures in 1973 by the International Astronomical Union. These names do not replace the classical names, but refer to *structures* instead of the albedo features indicated on earlier maps. In coming years the International Astronomical Union will make further selections and possible modifications of names for the newly revealed Martian features.

NASA SP-337

THE NEW MARS
The Discoveries of Mariner 9

WILLIAM K. HARTMANN AND ODELL RAPER

With the cooperation of
the Mariner 9 Science Experiment Team

Prepared for the NASA Office of Space Science

Scientific and Technical Information Office
NATIONAL AERONAUTICS AND SPACE ADMINISTRATION
Washington, D.C. 1974

For sale by the Superintendent of Documents
U.S. Government Printing Office, Washington, D.C. 20402
Price $8.75
Stock No. 3300–00577
Library of Congress Catalog Card No. 74-600084

Foreword

Mars, our planetary neighbor that gleams redly in the night sky, has intrigued man ever since he first began to study the heavens. The first telescopes brought exciting images of white polar caps that expanded and contracted with the seasons. In the 19th century, telescopes employed at the limits of useful resolution introduced the controversial "canals," with their radical implication, at least to Percival Lowell, of an advanced civilization struggling to survive in an increasingly arid world. In 1965 Mariner 4, the first flyby spacecraft, returned 22 images that in their limited field of view suggested that Mars might be a cratered, moonlike, dead planet. The 1969 flyby missions added rich detail and complexity. Then the 11-month scrutiny of Mars by Mariner 9—by all odds the most productive planetary mission that has ever been flown—provided us with a revolutionary new concept of the red planet.

We now perceive that Mars is an active, evolving planet. In some areas it is characterized by gigantic volcanoes, bigger than any on Earth, and in other areas by immense canyons of totally unprecedented length and depth. It is a world etched by wind erosion and patterned by eolian deposits in some places it seems to have been dissected by a fluid erosion of undetermined nature. The scientific achievements of the Mariner 9 mission have been enormous, establishing new benchmarks in our understanding of the solar system.

It would be shortsighted to think of this voyage of planetary exploration, for all its productivity, as providing no more than additional data about one distant world. We are discovering that knowing more about Mars gives us insight about more than Mars. To learn about neighboring planets leads to improved understanding of the entire solar system, including the planet Earth. This is because planetary exploration provides a vast new laboratory in which scientists in many disciplines can create and test conceptions of the origin and evolution of the solar system and the dynamic processes that have affected all planets. Theories can be derived, compared with known effects of known processes, modified, verified, or discarded. From distant planets we are gaining significant new understanding of such down-to-earth subjects as volcanism, plate tectonics, seismic instability, magnetic-field generation, and the dynamics of planetary atmosphere. From these studies and from the future exploration of Mars and other planets will come the answers that our children and grandchildren will need to keep Earth a comfortable abode in space for man.

JOHN E. NAUGLE
Associate Administrator for Space Science
National Aeronautics and Space Administration

JANUARY 14, 1974

Acknowledgment

The authors wish to thank Alice Agnieray, Anne Hartley, Susan James, Ermine van der Wyk, and Barbara Conn for assistance in preparing the manuscript and illustrations; the artists Chesley Bonestell, Don Davis, and Ludek Pesek, their publishers, and Morrison Planetarium for assistance in making their work available; William Baum of Lowell Observatory, Elmer Christianson of the Jet Propulsion Laboratory, and Steven Larson of the Lunar and Planetary Laboratory for assisting with photographic material; Ray Bradbury for his encouraging remarks; and Mariner 9 team members and associates J. Briggs, C. Chapman, J. Cutts, M. Davies, D. Davis, E. Glahn, H. Hipsher, C. Leovy, E. Miner, B. Murray, C. Sagan, R. Steinbacher, and T. Vrebalovich for assistance and helpful criticism of the text.

WILLIAM K. HARTMANN
Planetary Science Institute
ODELL RAPER
Jet Propulsion Laboratory

Mariner 9 Science Experiment Team

Television

*Masursky, H.
   Arthur, D.
   Batson, R.
   Borgeson, W.
   Carr, M.
   McCauley, J.
   Milton, D.
   Soderblom, L.
   Wildey, R.
   Wilhelms, D.
†Lederberg, J.
   Levinthal, E.
   Pollack, J.
   Sagan, C.
   Veverka, J.
†de Vaucouleurs, G.
   Young, A.
†Briggs, G.
   Shipley, E.
*Smith, B.
   Cutts, J.
   Davies, M.
   Hartmann, W.
   Leighton, R.
   Leovy, C.
   Murray, B.
   Sharp, R.

Infrared Interferometer Spectrometer

†Hanel, R.
   Conrath, B.
   Hovis, W.
   Kunde, V.
   Levin, G.
   Lowman, P.
   Pearl, J.
   Prabhakara, C.
   Schlachman, B.

Infrared Radiometer

†Neugebauer, G.
   Chase, S.
   Kieffer, H.
   Miner, E.
   Munch, G.

Ultraviolet Spectrometer

†Barth, C.
   Hord, C.
   Lane, A.
   Stewart, I.

Celestial Mechanics

†Lorell, J.
   Anderson, J.
   Martin, W.
   Sjogren, W.
†Shapiro, I.
   Reasenberg, R.

S-Band Occultation

†Kliore, A.
   Cain, D.
   Fjeldbo, G.
   Rasool, S.
   Seidel, B.

* Team leaders.
† Principal investigator. (The coinvestigators are indented beneath each principal investigator.)

Contents

CHAPTER I

Mars Before Mariner

In questions of science the authority of a thousand is not worth the humble reasoning of a single individual.
—ATTRIBUTED TO GALILEO

One is permitted to say crazy things at least two times a year.
—SCHIAPARELLI, QUOTED BY FLAMMARION

Those of us who grew up reading Wells or Burroughs or Bradbury or Clarke—or other writers of sufficient imagination to allow their characters to travel to or from Mars—have always known that Mars was a special target. Mars was said to be the planet where we might find life. Yet as we studied the concrete observational data in the last few decades, the supporting evidence for life on Mars seemed ever more elusive. By the mid-sixties the prospects seemed dim indeed. Telescopic observations showed the present state of Mars to be drier and more severe than the optimistic estimates of the early writers, who in turn based their settings on the estimates of still earlier scientists.

In 1971 and 1972, Mariner 9 revolutionized our conceptions. Before we can see how this came about, we have to understand how, through continually refined limits imposed by observations, we reached the pre-Mariner conception of Mars.

The first telescopic observations of Mars are believed to be those of Galileo, who, in 1610, wrote that he had detected the disk and phases of Mars, showing that it was a sensibly spherical body illuminated by the Sun. Lacking photography, early observers could record the appearance of the Martian surface only by carefully made sketches. The first of these was produced by the Italian scholar Francisco Fontana in 1636. Unfortunately, Fontana's telescope was too poor to show true details of the surface although he, too, recorded the phases. It was not until October 13, 1659, that the Dutch physicist Christiaan Huygens produced what Percival Lowell later called "the first drawing of Mars worthy of the name ever made by man." For the first time this showed one of Mars' characteristic dusky markings, probably the dark triangular region now known as Syrtis Major. The early observers assumed that the dark markings on Mars (and even on the Moon) were bodies of water and referred to them as *"maria"* (the Latin word for "seas").

During the rest of the 1600's, Renaissance scientists such as Cassini, Hooke, and others from all over Europe produced numerous observations of Mars. By 1666 Cassini and others deduced a rotation period of close to 24 hours —the same as Earth's—by following the motion of the spots and other markings. It was found that bright white caps marked the two poles and that the caps alternated in growing to a maximum size, depending on which hemisphere of Mars was experiencing winter. During Martian summer, the caps shrunk or disappeared.

By the early 1700's the drawings of Mars began to approach the quality of modern drawings. Finer patterns of dusky markings were recorded, having shapes that can still be identified today. A 1719 drawing by Maraldi shows a dark

Mars passing near the Moon. This photograph illustrates the difficulty of observing details on Mars from Earth. The planet appears no larger than a modest-sized lunar crater. (Lowell Observatory)

band that appeared to border the bright polar cap, a phenomenon later given much attention. Maraldi also noted changes that he thought might involve clouds.

In the late 1700's, the English astronomer William Herschel speculated that the dark band near the polar cap, which came to be known as the "polar melt band," was the product of melting ice or snow that composed the caps. Herschel noted that the caps could not be too thick because they nearly disappear in summer. Herschel also observed bright, changeable patches, which he took to be "clouds and vapors floating in the atmosphere of the planet." From his observations of the polar caps he deduced the inclination of Mars' axis to its orbital plane. Finally, Herschel and the German observer Schroeter in the 1780's and 1790's began to record narrow

streaky markings such as a curving "tail" on Syrtis Major.

It is interesting to note the conception of Mars that was transmitted by astronomers to other intellectuals of the early 1800's. Mars was a planet with oceans and lakes, dry reddish land, clouds, polar snows, a day of some 24 hours—in short, it was a planet much like Earth. In view of the momentous import attached by us moderns to the search for life in the universe, it may come as some surprise to realize that Herschel and other scientists of his time almost casually assumed that Mars and other planetary bodies were inhabited. This was before Darwin gave us the idea of the long struggle toward sentient life; thus scientists of the 19th century inherited the idea of "the plurality of worlds," with a Mars already teeming with creatures and a reasonably pleasant environment well suited for them.

In 1840 the Germans Wilhelm Beer and Johann Mädler published the first global charts of Mars. Other maps followed. While many features are easily recognizable today, some areas show systematic differences that undoubtedly reflect long-term changes. In 1863 Father Pietro Angelo Secchi in Rome published the first known color sketches.

About 1867 the physicists Pierre Jules Janssen and Sir William Huggins made the first attempt to detect oxygen and water vapor in the Martian atmosphere by searching for telltale absorptions in the planet's spectrum, but the attempt was inconclusive.

In 1869, Father Secchi referred to some of the streaklike Martian markings as *"canali,"* a term probably chosen to maintain the convention that dark areas were named after bodies of water.

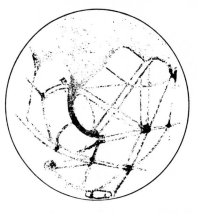

One of the earliest known sketches of Mars. It was drawn by Christian Huygens on November 28, 1659. The northward-extending marking is believed to be Syrtis Major.

Drawing of Mars by W. R. Dawes during the 1864–65 opposition. Syrtis Major extends toward the north, and the north polar hood is indicated.

Mars as drawn by Giovanni Schiaparelli on June 4, 1888. Syrtis Major extends north just below and to the left of center. Schiaparelli's system of *"canali,"* including many double canals, can be contrasted with the streaky markings shown by Dawes in the previous drawing.

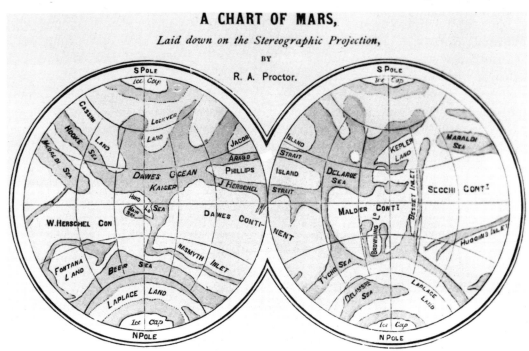

R. A. Proctor's map of Mars, published in 1871. South is at the top, a convention adopted by users of (inverting) astronomical telescopes. Syrtis Major is centered in the left hemisphere, bearing the now-discarded title "Kaiser Sea."

This term was later to become the key to the most famous astronomical controversy in history.

By 1871, so many Martian surface features were known that the English observer Richard Proctor produced a map with names attached to them. Proctor's proposed nomenclature was somewhat confusing, using the names of famous observers for all features. "Dawes' Ocean" and "Kaiser Sea," for example, were designations covering the most famous dark marking, now known as Syrtis Major.

A banner year for Martian studies was 1877. The confusion over nomenclature and Proctor's alleged bias toward English observers led Giovanni Schiaparelli, director of an observatory in Milan, to invent a new scheme of nomenclature. He applied it to his observations made during the unusually close approach—or opposition—of Mars in the summer of 1877. A classical scholar, Schiaparelli took names from historic and mythical sources of the classical Mediterranean world. These names, if difficult to grasp readily, have a marvelous quality. The most prominent dark area became Syrtis Major, named after a Mediterranean bay. Egyptian gods (Thoth, Isis, Anubis), biblical lands (Eden, Hiddekel), the Greek muses and sirens (Aonius Sinus, Mare Sirenum), and hell (Styx, Hades, Trivium Charontis) all found their way onto Mars. The dark areas were still oceanic, while the bright areas were named after terrestrial lands. Curiously enough, because Schiaparelli chose names from the Mediterranean world, Martian bright regions received names such as Arabia and Libya, thus by chance being named for arid, wind-blown, volcanic terrestrial deserts; Mariner 9 later revealed that these are among the closest terrestrial analogs to their Martian namesakes, in terms of geology.

The second outstanding event of 1877 was also the first major American contribution to the story of Mars. At the U.S. Naval Observatory, Asaph Hall discovered that Mars had two satellites, which he named "Phobos" and "Deimos" (fear and terror) after the horses that drew the chariot of the god of war. From their faintness it was clear that the two moons were only a few miles or tens of miles across—mere chunks of rock.

A third development in 1877 was the English observer N. Green's identification of white spots near the limb of Mars as morning and evening clouds that extended well above the Martian surface.

The fourth result of the 1877 opposition of Mars was the popularization of the most famous —or notorious—bit of Martian lore. In accounts of his observations published in 1878, Schiaparelli casually used Father Secchi's term *canale* (singular) and *canali* (plural) to refer to streaks that he had recorded. But Schiaparelli gave the idea a new character. (He is often incorrectly described as its originator, but Schiaparelli himself pointed out that "many of these *canali* are not new and have already been seen by such excellent observers as Kaiser, Lockyer, Secchi, Green, etc. . . .") Schiaparelli saw more of them and talked more about them than the other observers had. For example, he wrote of "a gulf ending in a sharp point. . . . The *canale* which originates there . . . is not easy to see and some uncertainty may arise concerning it." What an understatement! Schiaparelli's prediction of some uncertainty was to stretch into a

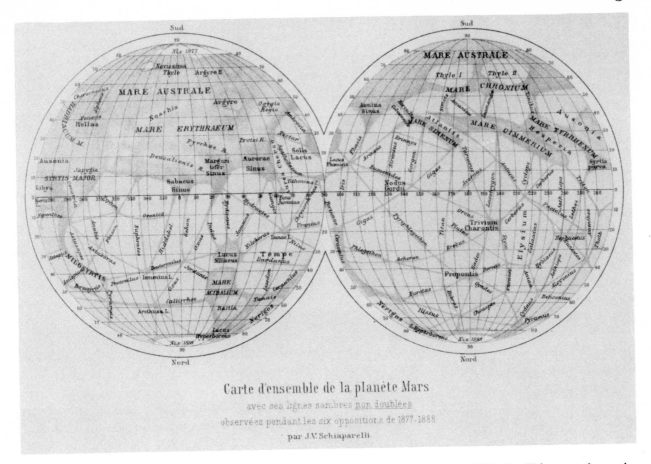

Carte d'ensemble de la planète Mars
avec ses lignes sombres non doublées
observées pendant les six oppositions de 1877-1888
par J.V.Schiaparelli

Schiaparelli's map of Mars, based on observations in 1877–88. This map shows the nomenclature introduced by Schiaparelli and since adopted by other observers. Syrtis Major is at the extreme left; south is at the top. The map shows the system of linear "canali" popularized by Schiaparelli.

60-year argument between observers who saw what they took to be "canals" and observers who could make out nothing of the sort.

In the following year, 1879, Mars was again in place for observation, and Schiaparelli, looking for one of the canals he had mapped in 1877, was astonished to see two parallel canals in its place. This doubling phenomenon came to be known as "gemination" in the literature of the late 1800's. No one else had seen any canals, let alone double ones. As Percival Lowell later wrote,

For nine years [Schiaparelli] labored thus alone, having his visions all to himself. It was not until 1886 that anyone but he saw the canals. In April of that year Perrotin at Nice first did so. . . . Perrotin was on the point of abandoning the search for good, when, on the 15th of the month, he suddenly detected one of the canals. the Phison. His assistant, N. Thillon, saw it immediately afterward. After this they managed to make out some others, some single, some double, substantially as Schiaparelli had drawn them. . . .

Observers from Italy, France, England, and the United States also claimed to see canals in 1886.

Here, then, was a strange new Mars, with networks of fine streaks crossing the bright areas, which had come to be known as deserts, and passing also through the dark regions. It seems that the more the observers studied the canals, the narrower and straighter the canals became. The canals were supposed, then, to be barely within the resolving power of the best telescopes under the best conditions; they appeared only during moments of superseeing.

Once the canals were widely reported, they quickly became the center of observers' discussions. What could be their explanation? In the 1890's many attempts were made to answer this question. Abbé Moreaux and a geologist associate in 1890 made globes that they inflated, causing pressure to crack the surfaces. The resulting crack patterns they likened to canals. In 1892 appeared a mammoth work, *La Planète Mars*, by Camille Flammarion, who gathered and discussed observations spanning 3½ centuries, including those of canals. In the same year the American observer W. H. Pickering first detected and defined Martian oases, which were small round dark spots said to lie at the junctions of the canals.

Among other observers straining to see the canals was E. E. Barnard, at Lick Observatory. Barnard, whom the late astronomer G. P. Kuiper called one of the most acute observers of all time, had a telescope with about twice the aperture of Schiaparelli's. On September 11, 1894, Barnard reported his efforts in a letter to Simon Newcomb:

I have been watching and drawing the surface of Mars. It is wonderfully full of detail. There is certainly no question about there being mountains and large greatly elevated plateaus. To save my soul I can't believe in the canals as Schiaparelli draws them. I see details where he has drawn none. I see details where some of his canals are, but they are not straight lines *at all*. When best seen these details are very irregular and broken up—that is, some of the regions of his canals; I verily believe—for all the verifications—that the canals as depicted by Schiaparelli are a fallacy and that they will be so proved before many favorable oppositions are past.

Barnard's skepticism was soon to be drowned out by the flood of attention directed toward the canals by other observers, particularly Percival Lowell.

Percival Lowell, traveler, member of a wealthy Boston family, and writer on the Far East, founded an observatory in the exceptionally clear, high-altitude air of Flagstaff, Ariz., in 1894. After a year of observing, he announced confirmation of the canals, the geminations, and the oases, and published a popular book, *Mars*. Lowell, an excellent writer, described both his observations and his interpretation of them with an extraordinary hypothesis. As for the canals, he stated,

Singular as each line looks to be by itself, it is the systematic network of the whole that is most amazing. Each line not only goes with wonderful directness from one point to another, but at this latter spot it contrives to meet, exactly, another line which has come with like directness from quite another direction.

While most observers would question whether this is really a description of Mars, it is undeniably a fine description of Lowell's drawings of Mars, by the artist himself. In a bit of interobservatory one-up-manship, Lowell claimed four times as many canals as were recorded on Schiaparelli's charts, a result he attributed to the superb Flagstaff observing conditions.

Lowell went on to picture the planet as a dying, drying world late in its evolution because of its smaller size and faster cooling rate. Little water was left on the once humid surface, he said, and so it followed that—

If . . . the planet possesses inhabitants, there is but one course open to them in order to support life. Irrigation, and upon as vast a scale as possible, must be the all-engrossing Martian pursuit. So much is directly deductible from what we have learned at Flagstaff of the physical condition of the planet. . . .

To illustrate the way Lowell built up his argument, it might be noted that these words appear on the last page of the chapter before the discussion of canals. In succeeding chapters the once innocuous term *canali* becomes the physical interpretation; the linear markings are irrigation canals constructed by intelligent beings to bring water from the poles to the more temperate equator. The idea was admittedly straightforward. Lowell ridiculed alternate ideas that had been put forward:

Snow caps of solid carbonic acid gas (CO_2), a planet cracked in a positively monomaniacal manner . . . hypotheses each more astounding than its predecessor. . . .

So the Victorians passed to the 20th century the possibility of a Mars with dwindling water and a civilization attempting to save itself by building irrigation systems. People discussed means of communicating with the Martians and began to conceive of Earth as viewed from a cosmic vantage point. Tennyson wrote,

Hesper—Venus—were we native to that
    splendour or in Mars
We should see the Globe we groan in,
    fairest of their evening stars.

Could we dream of wars and carnage, craft
    and madness, lust and spite,
Roaring London, raving Paris,
    in that point of peaceful light?

While British physicist George Johnstone Stoney was attempting to defend the idea that the polar caps might be frozen CO_2 (dry ice) in 1898, British novelist H. G. Wells published *The War of the Worlds,* in which Martians send expeditionary forces in capsules to land on Earth and decimate its population. (The Martians were finally defeated not by man's technology but by infection with terrestrial bacteria.) Thus while the most cautious scientists debated in the journals, the man in the street read of canal networks and invaders from Mars, and the seeds of a hundred grade B monster movies were sown.

While the study of Mars in the 1890's provides one of the best illustrations of the transmission of science to the public through various entertaining but rather distorting filters, this is not to say that there was not a legitimate scientific puzzle of great excitement. What was Mars like? Could it sustain life? Were the canals real? There was great excitement but there were few solid empirical facts.

Lowell defended artificial canals in two books published in 1906 and 1908. In 1907, Alfred Russell Wallace, who had conceived of Darwinian evolution independently of Darwin, published a book attacking Lowell's ideas. He stated that cracks must form on any planet with a hot, stable core and a cooling crust, thus forming an apparent "canal" network. Remarking on the very low, subfreezing temperature expected on Mars, Wallace concluded that no water vapor can exist and that "Mars . . . is absolutely uninhabitable."

In 1909 Camille Flammarion published the second volume of his encyclopedia of Martian observations, containing 426 drawings and 16 maps from the period 1890 to 1901. Flammarion struggled to make sense out of the mass of different impressions of the planet.

Flammarion and his contributors discussed all of the problems then current. For example, E. W. Maunder, of the Greenwich Observatory, calculated the atmospheric structure on the basis of gravity and relative mass of Mars. Because of the lower gravity, the Martian atmosphere would be more extended and have only about 40 percent the surface pressure of Earth's atmosphere, even if it had the same mass. If the Martian atmosphere were less massive in proportion to the planetary mass it would have about 14 percent the surface pressure, resembling Earth's atmosphere at nearly 50 000 feet. Because of the distance of Mars from the Sun, Maunder estimated temperatures as low as −135° Celsius (−211° Fahrenheit). At best, Maunder thought a day on Mars could be no more attractive than a day on a 20 000-foot mountain in Spitsbergen. Maunder's Mars was clearly not so hospitable as Lowell's

W. H. Pickering, using Lowell's telescope, reported that the dark areas generally appeared depressed when seen at the sunrise or sunset line and concluded,

Perhaps we are on the eve of constructing an orographic map of the planet, but these observations are very difficult and one must not expect too great precision. . . . There are hills and valleys and consequently the dark regions do not represent the surface of an ocean.

Louis Jewell at Johns Hopkins reported a new attempt to get spectroscopic evidence for oxygen and water vapor on Mars. Jewell concluded that the upper limit that could be set for oxygen was one-fourth that of Earth's atmosphere and for water vapor, an amount considerably greater than that of Earth.

As for the question of life on Mars, Schiaparelli himself contributed a discussion to Flammarion's book. Schiaparelli and others had noted that if the polar caps were frozen water, the fact that they melted in summer indicated a much warmer climate than Maunder had hypothesized. As Flammarion paraphrased,

Everything leads one to think that the climate of Mars is the same as that of our high mountains —very warm in the full sunlight of the day, very cold during the night. No clouds in general, no rains, just some sky and some snow.

Schiaparelli took a middle road on the question of life:

Geometric design [of the canals] lead[s] one to believe the work was done by intelligent beings . . . [yet] the bodies in Saturn's ring definitely were not turned out on a lathe. . . . Geometric forms are the simple and necessary consequences of the laws which govern the physical and physiological world.

It would be easier to satisfy oneself [as to the appearance. geminations, and variability of the canals and associated features] by introducing the action of organic forces. Here the field of hypotheses grows larger and infinite combinations present themselves. Changes in vegetation . . . generations of small animals. . . . Let us hope and continue to study.

Clearly the discussion had gone as far as it could (or farther) without substantial new scientific information. So strongly had Lowell emphasized the advantages of excellent atmospheric conditions and optics, that opinion was heavily swayed by the reports of observers with big telescopes in good locations. G. E. Hale and his associates turned the 60-inch telescope of Mount Wilson toward Mars on November 3, 1909, during a period of excellent conditions when 800-power magnification could be used. They reported "not a trace of geometrical structure on the planet, nor any narrow straight canals." This observation was widely quoted by observers who could not confirm the straight, Lowellian canals.

A similar result was later reported by the French observer E. M. Antoniadi, who described his impression at a 32¾-inch telescope on September 20, 1909:

At the first glance . . . [I] thought [I] was dreaming and scanning Mars from his outer satellite. The planet revealed a prodigious and bewildering amount of sharp or diffused natural, irregular, detail, all steadily; and it was at once obvious that the geometrical network of single or double canals discovered by Schiaparelli was a gross illusion. Such detail could not be drawn; hence only its coarser markings were recorded in the note-book.

Such reports marked the beginning of a reversal in the discussions. Nonetheless, it was later pointed out in rebuttal that the Hale and Antoniadi observations were made at a midsummer season on Mars (Martian effective date July 23 for Hale) when canals were not usually prominent. Observers who detected canals reported that they were most prominent during late spring (Martian dates April 1 to June 15 for the northern hemisphere).

In 1913, E. W. Maunder published his famous "English schoolboy experiment" in which a classroom of some 200 pupils unaware of the elements of the controversy sketched from their seats at various distances a set of Martian drawings which contained no linear canals, but in their place "a few dots or irregular markings . . . here and there." The closest pupils drew the spots; the farthest could not see any of the fine markings, but the intermediate students made out systems of nonexistent straight lines. This supported a growing suspicion that Mars contained a variety of surface detail just on the limits of resolution from Earth, so that observers in the best moments of seeing mistakenly perceived lines instead of the actual poorly alined splotches and shadings.

During the 1924 and 1926 appearances of Mars, the American observer Trumpler, using the 36-inch Lick telescope, wrote,

[Canals] vary greatly in visibility, width, and definition. . . . Practically every step of transition between . . . broad bands and the finest most difficult canals is represented. The canals . . . do not appear quite sharp, but rather as diffuse hazy shadings.

This again was quite a different description than that given by Lowell, who had popularized the canals as finely etched straight lines.

During the same years, W. H. Wright of Lick and E. C. and V. M. Slipher of Lowell obtained the first good series of photographs in various colors. These showed that just as on Earth, red light penetrated farthest through the atmosphere, while blue light was reflected or scattered from the atmosphere, hazes, and clouds. Photographs through blue filters did not show the surface features of Mars, but rather showed a hazy surface with occasional cloud features. Martian dark markings showed most clearly with the reddest filters but were sometimes obscured by yellowish clouds assumed to be blowing dust.

At the same time Nicholson and Pettit at Mount Wilson and Coblentz and Lampland at Lowell got the first good measurements of the thermal radiation of Mars, giving the following temperatures:

South polar cap	−70° Celsius (−94° Fahrenheit)
Sunset	−13° Celsius (9° Fahrenheit)
Noon (subsolar)	10° Celsius (50° Fahrenheit)

The mean temperature on Mars, on the basis of such measurements, was interpreted to be −40° Celsius (−40° Fahrenheit), as opposed to a terrestrial mean temperature of about 15° Celsius (59° Fahrenheit).

In 1930 the French observer E. M. Antoniadi published a compendium of Martian observational data, *La Planète Mars,* which contained a new detailed map and stressed that in regions where earlier observers had reported canals, he himself, using the largest refracting telescope in Europe, had seen only irregular patchy arrays of spots and splotches that merely seemed linear under poorer conditions. This became the most definitive word on canals, as far as Earth-based telescopic observation was concerned.

There remained, of course, the question of the cause of the large-scale, variable dark markings on Mars. Because of their seasonal varia-

tions and reputed greenish color, the hypothesis of Martian vegetation remained attractive. What was needed to confirm or refute this idea was more discriminating observational tests. In 1938, the Canadian astronomer Peter M. Millman began a spectroscopic study of the markings by noting,

. . . so much nonsense has been written about the planet in various branches of literary endeavor, that it is easy to forget that Mars is still the object of serious scientific investigation. . . .

Millman considered the spectrum of the light reflected from the dark areas separately from that of the light reflected from the bright regions. Just as Wright's photographs in 1924 had shown the dark markings to be most pronounced in red light, Millman found that the greatest contrast in his photographic spectra appeared at red wavelengths near 6000 angstroms. On the other hand, he noted that all leafy vegetation on Earth is bright rather than dark at red wavelengths because of chlorophyll's transparency in red and resultant multiple scattering of red light. This difference between Earth's plants and Martian dark areas was a substantial argument against the dark markings being vegetated areas.

More data came from the oppositions of 1934, 1937, and 1941, during which W. S. Adams and T. Dunham, using the 100-inch reflector on Mount Wilson, were able to reduce still further the limits for oxygen and water vapor on Mars. After finding no O_2 or H_2O absorptions in the best spectra yet obtained, they concluded that the oxygen content was less than 1 percent the quantity above Earth's surface and that the water vapor content of the Martian atmosphere was similarly low. Not only the temperature but also the atmospheric conditions were more hostile than had once been assumed.

It is interesting to note the steady drift away from the conception of a habitable Mars. Near 1800, Herschel had assumed a fertile, inhabited planet. By 1900 the conception was that the Martians had to struggle against arid environment for their existence, if they existed at all. By 1940, evidence was beginning to accumulate against vigorous plant life, not to mention intelligent creatures.

Nonetheless, the peculiarity of the markings on Mars (as compared with those on the Moon,

for example) could not easily be dismissed. They changed both seasonally and sporadically. Even the "canals" were still a subject of discussion. For example, Edison Pettit of Mount Wilson, who had never seen "canals" during his observations of Mars with large telescopes, finally reported them during a series of observations with a 6-inch refracting telescope, undertaken for his own education. One morning in 1939 a linear feature became visible, followed in seconds by another. Pettit attributed the visibility of canals to moments of superseeing, which came only rarely. His report to some extent reopened the debate about the canal question; there was the nagging suspicion that

A proposed solution to the problem of the "canals." In the left drawing, E. M. Antoniadi shows markings under the very best observing conditions in the region south of Elysium (bright oval, top). On the right, the same region is shown as drawn by earlier observers under poorer conditions when dark "nuclei" and color boundaries are seen as streaks.

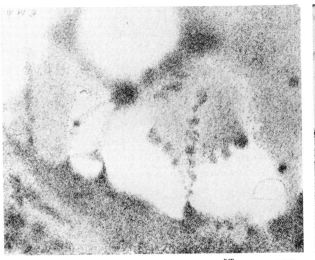 

0 km   1000   2000   5000

unusual linear features or alinements did exist in some form on Mars, and might be variable in their prominence because of seasonal or non-seasonal real changes on the surface of Mars.

In the 1940's, G. P. Kuiper at the McDonald Observatory took advantage of newly developed infrared detectors to study parts of the spectrum even redder than had been studied before. In these infrared regions, carbon dioxide, water vapor, and other gases have diagnostic absorptions. In 1947, for the first time, Kuiper identified one of the Martian gases, carbon dioxide. Some other gases such as nitrogen, which composes 78 percent of Earth's atmosphere (by volume), could not be ruled out because they exhibit no spectral absorption bands in the region of the spectrum studied. Oxygen was virtually absent and water vapor very scarce. In view of the uncertainty about such potentially major constituents as nitrogen, it was difficult to estimate the total surface pressure of the Martian atmosphere.

In 1950 the astronomer E. J. Öpik reviewed the current observations and emphasized that the dark markings must be continually renewed by some mechanism, because photographic and visual records proved that certain dark regions had disappeared only to reappear several months or years later. This revived interest in the idea that some low form of biological activity might be involved in renewing the markings; dark bare rock would not regenerate by itself if once covered by light-colored dust.

The search for specific rock or soil materials that might account for the known properties of the Martian surface was advanced in 1950 when the French observer A. Dollfus reported that of many soil samples, the only one that matched the color, brightness, and polarimetric qualities of the bright areas on Mars was a sample of powdered limonite, a hydrated iron oxide formed in arid regions on Earth. A powdery or dusty texture was required and was consistent with the yellowish hazes said to be "dust storms." Other rock types such as red sandstone and various volcanic ashes did not match the data as well. This observation supported the longstanding theory that the reddish color of Mars was due to oxidation of iron-bearing surface minerals, as occurs in the orangish deserts of Earth.

In 1951 the French observer Gerard de Vaucouleurs published the most recent technical book-length monograph on Mars, which was subsequently translated into an English edition in 1954, *Physics of the Planet Mars*. This contained not only a review of observations through 1952 but also material on the theoretical meteorology, climatology, and internal structure of Mars.

In 1952, Kuiper published a summary of his infrared studies of the planet. He interpreted his spectra of the polar caps as solving the old problem of whether the caps were frozen water or frozen CO_2—i.e., dry ice. Kuiper found that his spectra matched the appearance of water frost, and not dry ice. Concluding that the caps contained water ice, he proposed a model of the Martian atmosphere with floating ice crystals, ranging up to some 10 or 15 kilometers above the surface, responsible for the well-known bluish hazes that partly obscure the planet. Yellowish hazes were taken to be blowing dust. Kuiper further concluded from colors and spectral features that "the bright regions of Mars are composed of igneous rock, similar to felsitic rhyolite," a brownish rock that matched the spectra better than red soils or volcanic ash samples. Taking into account the emphasis by Öpik and others on the variability of the dark regions, Kuiper discussed the possibility that lichens—a symbiotic plant combining fungi and algae and frequently found on bare rock in a wide range of climates including Antarctica—were responsible for the dark markings. Kuiper proposed that lichens might account for the color and regenerative properties, although they do not display as strong a seasonal variation as found on Mars.

In 1954, W. M. Sinton and J. Strong, using the 200-inch telescope on Mount Palomar, obtained new radiometer measurements of temperatures on Mars. These included—

Sunrise on equator . . . .   −60° Celsius
                                          (−76° Fahrenheit)
Noon on equator . . . .   25° Celsius
                                          (77° Fahrenheit)
Yellow cloud . . . . −25° Celsius
                                          (−1° Fahrenheit)

The year 1954 also saw publication in five astrononomical and geological journals of a new theoretical interpretation of the Martian markings, which, in the light of Mariner 9 knowledge, was one of the most accurate of the pre-Mariner general planetary models for the surface of Mars. Dean B. McLaughlin, of the University of Michigan, started by considering the general shape of the large dark masses. Instead of being roughly circular, as are the lunar maria (lava flows filling circular impact craters), the Martian markings are elongated, often with curving branches or streaky extensions lying at an angle to the equator. The pattern suggested to McLaughlin the trade wind patterns of Earth. Perhaps the markings were deposits of dark windblown dust, McLaughlin suggested. He next considered the common pointed extensions of Martian dark areas named "carets" by Lowell. Examples are the forks of the "forked bay," Sinus Meridiani. The tips of these, he reasoned, must be sources of dark powdery material that was then blown by prevailing winds and deposited in the characteristic funnel-shaped fans. McLaughin assumed that the sources were active volcanoes and that the dark windblown material was volcanic ash. The markings, then, were due to ash deposits maintained in certain patterns by the stable prevailing winds. The regenerative power of the dark markings was attributed to the eruption of volcanoes, at the tips of pointed markings, and their variability was attributed to local changes in deposition patterns due to wind shifts.

In 1955, Kuiper reviewed the available evidence on the surface markings and concluded that the dark areas were probably ultimately caused by ancient lavas, as on the Moon, but possibly covered in part by primitive plants. Kuiper argued against McLaughlin's notion of active volcanism as the essential cause of the changes because terrestrial volcanoes emit large amounts of water: volcanism at the rate required by McLaughlin would produce orders of magnitude more water on Mars than the amount observed in the spectroscopic results. Such arguments caused McLaughlin's hypothesis to lose favor in the 1950's. Instead, most

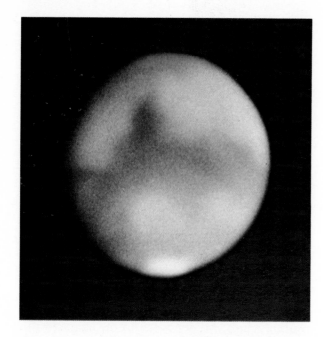

Two modern terrestrial photographs of Mars showing the face of the planet illustrated in some of the early drawings in this chapter. Syrtis Major is the darkest marking. The bright, pale oval area due south of Syrtis Major is the "desert" Hellas. The south polar cap and north polar haze are visible. (Lunar and Planetary Laboratory, University of Arizona)

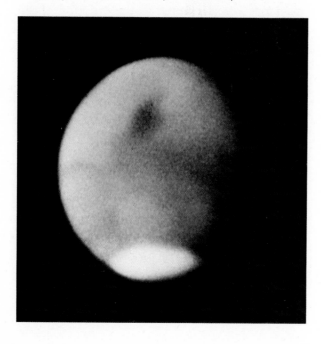

observers agreed at that time with Kuiper's conclusion:

The hypothesis of plant life . . . appears still the most satisfactory explanation of the various shades of dark markings and their complex seasonal and secular changes.

We will not continue to detail the myriad of new observational material that poured in after the beginning of the space age in 1957. This information will be presented in the topical chapters that follow. However, we will discuss two types of research that directly attacked the old question of life on Mars.

The profound ramifications of the hypothesis of plant life on Mars—i.e., the implication that life arises on any planet where conditions are clement, and could evolve to intelligence—of course led to many attempts to confirm or refute the idea. Clearly, proof of life on Mars would be one of the great discoveries of history.

The first type of research on this problem was directly observational. It was known that certain carbon-hydrogen molecular bonds in vegetation, particularly in chlorophyll, give rise to spectral absorptions far in the infrared, near wavelengths of 3.4 to 3.5 micrometers. After observations in 1956, the American observer W. M. Sinton announced confirmation of three of these absorption bands in the spectrum of Mars. This report, contained in a paper titled "Spectroscopic Evidence for Vegetation on Mars," caused a flurry of excitement. However, a few years later, Sinton, along with astronomers D. Rea and B. O'Leary, was able to identify two of the three bands as caused not by molecules on Mars but by molecules of heavy water (a rare form of H_2O containing an atom of

An early conception of the Martian landscape, as painted about 1946 by Chesley Bonestell, 2½ decades before Mariner 9. The orangish desert and distant dust cloud are consistent with modern views, but the green tones of the foreground are inconsistent with recent measurements. (From *The Conquest of Space* by Willy Ley and Chesley Bonestell. © 1947 by Chesley Bonestell. Reprinted by permission of The Viking Press, Inc.)

deuterium in place of one hydrogen atom) in Earth's atmosphere. By coincidence, the heavy water absorption bands happen to overlap the spectral positions of the sought-for Martian C–H bands. The third band that had been reported was so weak that its existence was questionable from the start. Thus, by the early 1960's, there appeared to be no spectroscopic evidence of complex organic materials on Mars.

A second type of research dealing with life on Mars was experimental. H. Strughold and his colleagues at the U.S. Air Force Aerospace Medical Division began experiments around 1957 to find out if simple terrestrial organisms could survive in the Martian environment. Of course, the test environment was a simulation of the Martian environment as it was conceived in 1957. Because the estimates of surface pressure declined markedly during the following decade, the experiments had to be repeated. In general, the results stayed the same: terrestrial microorganisms and spores could survive at least in a dormant state on Mars; growth and reproduction depended on the availability of moisture, ultraviolet light incidence, and similar environmental factors. Native Martian life forms, however, might conceivably have evolved by natural selection to a condition where they could flourish in the present Martian environment.

Quotations from several workers during this period sum up the prevalent attitudes. The biologist N. H. Horowitz in 1966 wrote,

... if we admit the possibility that Mars once had a more favorable climate ... we cannot exclude the possibility that Martian life succeeded in adapting itself to the changing conditions and remains there still.

In 1968, the chemist W. F. Libby, known for developing the radiocarbon method for archeological dating, commented,

Intelligent life as we know it can hardly be expected on the surface of . . . Mars . . . for two reasons—the extreme swing of temperature and the killing nature of unfiltered sunlight. So the possibility of life . . . would appear to be restricted to subterranean forms requiring no atmosphere and no sunlight. Our studies of meteoritic matter show that considerable quantities of organic matter, presumably primeval, exist, and we can think therefore of anaerobic bacteria living off of this matter. . . . Anaerobic subterranean life may be chemically possible on . . . Mars.

Finally, NASA biologists C. Ponnamperuma and H. P. Klein reviewed the knowledge of Mars as recently as 1970 and concluded,

. . . it seems clear that the limiting factor for life on [Mars] is likely to be the unavailability of water. Temperature fluctuations, low atmospheric pressures, lack of atmospheric oxygen . . . and increased radiation (even in the ultraviolet region), are all secondary to this point.

Future [experiments], particularly on the Mariner 1971 orbiting spacecraft, will survey the planet for local sources of water. . . .

New observations by substantially new techniques were now needed to go beyond the level of theorizing that had led observers closer to, but had not really produced, a complete understanding of the processes occurring on Mars. Investigation by spacecraft was to provide a quantum jump forward and shed new light on the key question of water and its behavior on the surface of Mars.

CHAPTER II

Summary of the Changing Face of Mars

A vast collection of facsimiles and information has been amassed.

—EARL C. SLIPHER, 1962

Before beginning a systematic topical review of the findings of the Mariner 9 mission, we must pause to summarize what was known of the peculiar, changing markings observed during the hundreds of years of data collecting described in chapter I. We will present this in the form of a discussion of four types of markings and their seasonal changes. We also take this opportunity to present several classical and recent maps of Mars as constructed by Earth-based observers without the benefit of spacecraft data. This material summarizes pre-Mariner knowledge on the basis of which the Mariner missions to Mars were conceived and planned. The four categories of markings—those which greet the observer who first looks at the planet with a large telescope—are polar caps, dark areas, bright areas, and clouds.

POLAR CAPS

At the end of summer on either hemisphere of Mars, a vast, whitish, diffuse haze forms over the polar region, extending as far as latitude 40° to 50°. The nature of these clouds was uncertain prior to Mariner 9. When this veil finally disappears at the end of winter, a brilliant white polar cap is exposed. Slowly it begins to shrink, and its rate of shrinkage increases as spring proceeds. By midspring on Mars, the cap begins to break into various sections, divided by dark rifts. Isolated patches may appear near the edge. Finally the summer cap shrinks to a small residual patch. Prior to Mariner 9 it was widely but incorrectly believed that the south cap disappeared entirely during summer, although de Vaucouleurs in 1954 noted that neither cap vanished. In late summer the polar haze forms again, first as patchy diffuse clouds, later merging into a uniform polar haze. The new cycle thus begins and repeats the old cycle with small variations from year to year. One of the main unresolved research questions about the cap concerns its composition. Clearly it is some frost or snowlike material, but in spite of Kuiper's 1952 assertion that the cap surface showed spectral features of water frost, later results suggested a large amount of frozen CO_2, or a mixture, the relative abundance of which was a key question for Mariner 9 in order to progress toward an understanding of the past availability of water on the surface of Mars.

DARK AREAS

The dark areas are called "maria" (singular, "mare"), the Latin word for seas, because the earliest observers thought they were oceans. Smaller dark areas are referred to as lakes (lacus), bays, etc. Although visual observers of the past usually described the dark areas as greenish or bluish in color, spectroscopic observations in the last decades—such as those by the French observer A. Dollfus and by T. McCord of MIT—have shown that they are merely less red than the bright areas. That is, they are brownish, or perhaps occasionally gray.

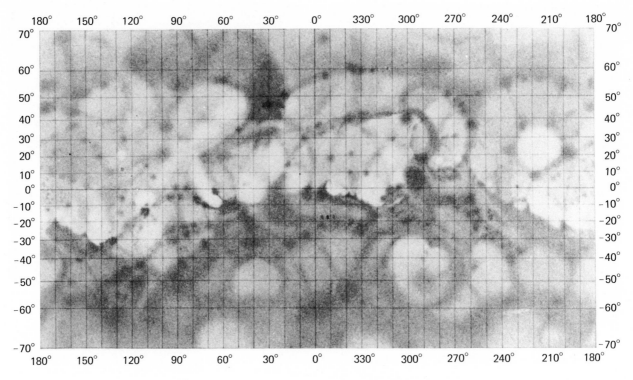

Map of Mars by the French observer E. M. Antoniadi, drawn in 1925. This map emphasizes the patchy nature of the dark markings and the spotty "nuclei" of which they are composed as seen visually from Earth under the best conditions.

Four faces of Mars as recorded in composite photographs, prepared by combining single-color images made with red, green, and blue filters. (Lowell Observatory International Planetary Patrol)

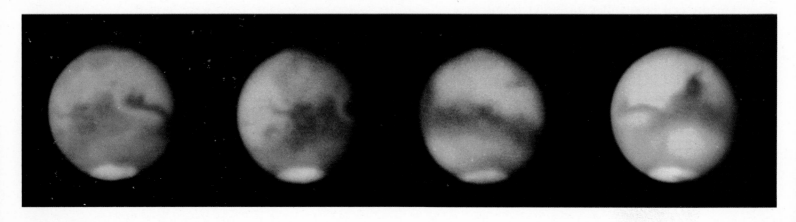

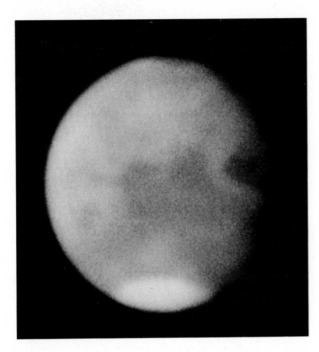

Region of Mare Erythraeum, photographed in 1971. (Lunar and Planetary Laboratory, University of Arizona)

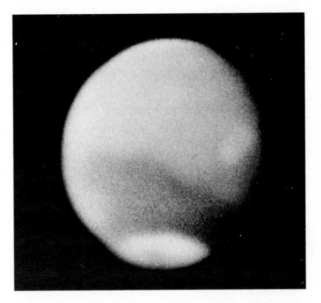

A bright cloud is visible at right, having formed in the Martian evening over the Tharsis area. A bright south polar cap is visible in this July 7, 1971, photograph, along with a bright south polar cap and some north polar haze. (Lunar and Planetary Laboratory, University of Arizona)

The subjective greenish tone may be a color-contrast effect caused by the markings being placed on an orangish background. Changes in the markings included sporadic changes in shape or darkness, and seasonal changes. One example of a sporadic change is the darkening and spreading since 1909 of a curved region (called a "canal" complex by some) east of Syrtis Major known as Thoth-Nepenthes. Another example is the changeability of the Solis Lacus region, which occasionally disappears only to re-form at some later date. Many such changes have been documented in a photographic atlas by E. C. Slipher of Lowell Observatory. Seasonal changes are just as remarkable. During the Martian winter, the markings are faint. As the polar cap begins to retreat in spring, a dark band is reported nearby, which then spreads toward the equator. Markings darken dramatically and become more clear and well defined. This phenomenon is called the "wave of darkening." De Vaucouleurs has reported a rate of 2.0 kilometers per hour (1.2 miles per hour) for the general wave, with considerably slower rates in certain dark "arteries," such as Hellespontus. That the darkening spreads from the polar cap as the cap itself diminishes was, of course, responsible for the early belief that some material from the cap itself was responsible for darkening. This led at once to the hypothesis that the mysterious material was water or water vapor, and that the darkening was a result of its action on vegetation. A counter argument is that even the earliest advocates of vegetation recognized a color change that accompanied the wave of darkening, and this change was from a grayish (or reportedly greenish) winter color to a brown or chocolate color in spring and summer—opposite from the terrestrial vegetation color changes. The obvious research question prior to the Mariner 9 mission concerned the exact nature of the dark material and the cause of the changes.

BRIGHT AREAS

Because these areas were thought by the first observers to be land, and because Mars is known to be dry, these areas acquired the name "desert"—a name certainly more fitting than the appellation "maria" for the dark regions. Although there has been a tendency to think of these areas as passive backdrop for the variable dark markings (perhaps the psychological response from sketching the dark markings on blank white paper), the bright areas have detail of their own. The Elysium area, for example, is often noticeably lighter than other areas. Yellowish dust veils seem to be associated with light areas, particularly Hellas. Recently, spectrophotometric observers such as P. Boyce of Lowell Observatory and T. McCord of MIT have reported that when the relative brightness of neighboring bright and dark areas changes, as in the case of Arabia and Syrtis Major the bright area may brighten rather than the dark area growing darker. Similarly, these observers report a common midafternoon brightening of the bright areas, suggesting that winds rise in the afternoon and stir up dust clouds. Some of these observations suggest, but do not prove, that the bright areas have significant amounts of fine mobile surface dust that can be easily stirred

by winds. The Mariner 9 mission was designed to allow photographic resolution of fine detail in the bright areas and to detect changes in brightness of markings.

CLOUDS

The relative permanence of the background markings on Mars makes it easy to detect clouds that temporarily obscure these markings. Such clouds have traditionally been divided into three categories: yellow clouds, white clouds, and bluish clouds and hazes. The yellow clouds have a relatively straightforward interpretation. Their color, their association to some extent with bright areas, and polarimetric observations by the French observer A. Dollfus and others all indicate that they are composed of fine yellowish dust particles, some micrometers (1 micrometer = 0.0001 centimeter) in diameter, raised from the surface of Mars by winds. White clouds have been thought to be condensation products; hypotheses include high cirruslike clouds of water ice crystals or frozen CO_2 crystals. Such clouds are sometimes associated with white patches that remain fixed, apparently lie on the ground, and are believed to be frost deposits. White clouds and frosts are often observed along the sunrise or sunset lines, but occur elsewhere. We will see that Mariner 9 gathered definitive new evidence on the nature of these clouds. Bluish clouds and hazes are a more controversial topic. Discrete blue clouds—so named because they were detected on photographs made with blue filters—are usually coincident with what visual observers call white clouds. However, an additional phenomenon is present because photographs in blue light almost always show a nearly blank haze obscuring the surface markings. On occasion, however, blue photographs show the markings almost as clearly as photographs made with red filters. For some years, many observers believed this so-called "blue clearing" occurred only at opposition, when Mars was in its full phase opposite in direction from the Sun; hence it was suggested that the blue clearing might be related to the phase of Mars. Other observers have discounted this relationship as an effect of observational selection. Slipher's photometric catalog shows examples of blue clearing far from opposition. It has been hypothesized that the surface markings of Mars are intrinsically low in contrast in blue light, accounting for the puzzling "blue haze" without actually invoking an atmospheric haze. However, this hypothesis does not account for a blue clearing, in which most, of the markings of a whole hemisphere can become visible in blue light. Alternately, the blue haze might be caused by the finest dust particles—of diameter less than half a micrometer—which because of their small size cause Rayleigh scattering and remain suspended in the atmosphere for months. The usual objection to this theory is that the clearings occur too fast to correspond to settling of such fine particles. Still another hypothesis discussed by S. L. Hess, G. P. Kuiper, and others is that the blue haze is formed by small crystals of frozen water or CO_2. Melting or subliming these could produce sudden clearings. The atmospheric nature of the blue haze is especially indicated by 1954 photographs in which, during partial clearings, crude zonal bands formed parallel to the equator, typical of global atmospheric circulation patterns. Slipher proposed that because these bands are less pronounced in the Martian afternoon, afternoon winds disrupted them. This idea is carried further by D. T. Thompson of Lowell Observatory, who proposes that part of the blue clearing is caused by the brightening of bright areas, usually in the Martian afternoon and following different behavior patterns in different parts of the planet. Mariner 9 was designed to carry out spectroscopic analysis, temperature sensing, and photography to clarify the nature of the blue hazes and other cloud phenomena.

CHAPTER III

Early Mariners and the Profile of the Mariner 9 Mission

. . . man has imagined that Mars, of all the planets, most closely resembles Earth. . . . Mariner 4 abruptly reversed these visions and suggested that Mars, heavily cratered and lacking Earth's dense atmosphere . . . more closely resembled the Moon. The Mariner 6 and 7 flights have finally revealed a unique Martian character, distinctly different from that of either the Earth or the Moon.

[These missions] have raised many new questions whose answers await the discoveries of future missions.

—S. A. COLLINS, 1971

On November 28, 1964, an Atlas/Agena rocket was launched from Cape Kennedy, carrying atop its second stage a spacecraft designated as "Mariner 4," which was destined to end the era of Martian studies limited exclusively to Earth-based observations. Unlike its sister ship Mariner 3, which had suffered a catastrophic failure 23 days earlier when the protective shroud failed to separate from the spacecraft after launch, Mariner 4 was successfully deployed on its planned course to Mars. The spacecraft payload consisted of an array of instruments for measuring particles and fields, which were operative throughout the interplanetary journey, and a single television camera for photographing the surface of the planet during encounter. In addition, an occultation experiment was planned, using the onboard radio. To perform this experiment, the spacecraft was intentionally targeted to pass behind Mars immediately after the flyby, thus allowing radio signals to pass through the Martian ionosphere and atmosphere. The changes in frequency, phase, and amplitude of the radio signals resulting from refraction by the atmosphere could then be studied and used to deduce atmospheric pressures, temperatures, and densities.

On July 15, 1965, at 18 minutes and 33 seconds past midnight Greenwich mean time, Mariner 4 shuttered man's first closeup picture of Mars. As the spacecraft flew by, 20 additional pictures of the planet's surface were shuttered, the last two falling completely beyond the terminator (sunset line) on the dark side. Following the planned occultation, playback of the taped pictures and other information began; because of the necessarily low data rate capability at the tremendous distance involved (more than 300 million kilometers), the first transmission of all the recorded data was not completed until 9½ days later, on July 24. However, by the time the first few pictures were received, it was already apparent that Mars was a different planet than that which hundreds of years of ground-based observations had led us to expect.

The most significant fact revealed by the Mariner 4 pictures was the distinctly lunar appearance of the Martian surface: in the 19 frames, several hundred craters were identified. Until that time, only a few scientists had considered the possibility that Mars might be heavily cratered, and their predictions were largely ignored. In addition, data from the occultation experiment yielded a 5- to 10-millibar surface pressure —much lower than predicted from most previous Earth-based observations—and an average mo-

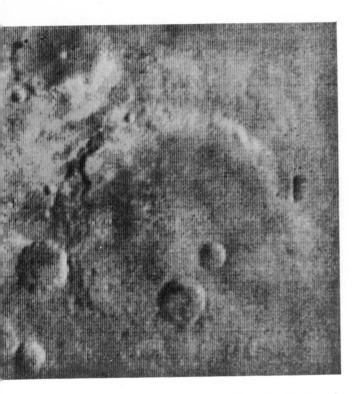

The first photographic mission to Mars, by Mariner 4, returned photographs of craters, such as this crater in the region of Atlantis.

lecular weight of 40, indicative of an atmosphere primarily composed of carbon dioxide. No significant changes in the particles and fields measurements were observed in the vicinity of the planet.

As Mariner 4 continued in its orbit around the Sun, scientists began a painstaking analysis of the data it had collected and transmitted to Earth. In terms of information theory, the amount of information contained in each of the Mariner pictures was nearly 20 times that of the best Earth-based photographs of the planet, but

this was still really not very much data: one ordinary snapshot, taken through a good lens, contains about 25 times as many information bits as the entire set of Mariner 4 pictures. In addition, the Mariner 4 pictures, although showing finer detail than ever before seen, showed only a very limited area of the planet, making planetwide generalizations extremely speculative.

Therefore, shortly after the successful Mariner 4 flyby, NASA authorized a second, more ambitious Mariner mission to Mars. Accordingly, two spacecraft with improved two-camera imaging systems and more complex science payloads were designed and built for a Mars flyby in late July and early August 1969. Designated Mariners 6 and 7,[1] both spacecraft were successfully launched and deployed on their proper trajectories. These trajectories were planned so that, although launched more than a month apart (on February 24 and March 27, 1969, respectively), the two spacecraft would encounter Mars 5 days apart.

Each spacecraft carried both a camera with a wide-angle lens and a camera with a telephoto lens. The telephoto lens covered a field of view one-tenth the size of that covered by the wide-angle lens, with a corresponding increase in angular resolution. In addition to the cameras, each spacecraft carried an ultraviolet spectrometer, an infrared spectrometer, and an infrared radiometer. In a complementary fashion, the spectrometers were capable of detecting and measur-

[1] Mariner 5, a single-launch mission, successfully flew by Venus in 1967. The first two Mariners were also Venus probes launched in 1962: Mariner 1 veered off course at launch and had to be destroyed by the range safety officer, but Mariner 2 successfully completed the mission.

ing many of the atomic, ionic, and molecular species potentially present in the atmosphere of Mars, including those considered to have biological significance. The radiometer was designed to measure surface temperatures and was boresighted with the imaging system, thus covering the same areas as the television pictures.

Two new features of the Mariner 6 and 7 spacecraft enhanced their capability over Mariner 4. The first of these, a two-degree-of-freedom scan platform, allowed the instruments to be pointed, extending the range over which the planet could be seen during encounter. The second innovation was an experimental high-rate telemetry system which, when used in conjunction with the then recently completed 64-meter antenna at Goldstone, Calif., provided a telemetry capability of 16 200 bits per second, 2000 times greater than Mariner 4. To take maximum advantage of these capabilities, the Mariner 6 and 7 encounters were planned in two phases, designated "far encounter" and "near encounter," with pictures being taken as early as 3 days before flyby and played back at intervals coincident with the Goldstone viewing periods. These far-encounter pictures would allow Martian coverage to provide a "missing link" in resolution between Earth-based and near-encounter Mariner pictures.

On July 29, Mariner 6 began photographing Mars. Late the following day it flew by the planet after having taken 50 far-encounter and 25 near-encounter pictures. Three days later, on August 2, Mariner 7 began its operations, successfully acquiring 91 far-encounter and 33 near-encounter pictures before passing beyond Mars on August 4. After their flybys, both Mariners passed behind Mars, providing four new occultation data points for subsequent analysis.

For the most part, the vastly improved Mariner 6 and 7 pictures tended to strengthen the somewhat tenuous conclusion derived from Mariner 4 results that lunarlike craters were widely scattered on Mars, although they also revealed that the Martian craters were more heavily modified by erosion processes than were those on the Moon. In addition, a few of the near-encounter photographs yielded evidence of two distinctly different types of terrain: the floor of Hellas, near the south polar cap, was apparently devoid of craters or any other terrain features, and a jumbled, broken type of terrain, unlike any known terrestrial or lunar topography, was observed in the near-equatorial region of Aurorae Sinus. The occultation results were consistent with the earlier results of Mariner 4, with surface pressures at the four occultation points ranging between 4 and 7 millibars. Data from the spectrometers confirmed the prediction, based on the Mariner 4 occultation experiment, that the Martian atmosphere was primarily CO_2, with only trace amounts of other gases being observed. Finally, the radiometer data revealed that the temperature of the south polar cap was consistent with the temperature of frozen carbon dioxide.

Even as the analyses of these data began, many of the same scientists involved in the task were already hard at work in planning for the next encounter with Mars. While Mariners 4, 6, and 7 had all been successful in fulfilling their mission objectives, each had provided only a brief and tantalizing glimpse of the planet's surface. Clearly, scores of such flybys would be needed to resolve the many mysteries still remaining. The alternative, as envisioned by NASA and the scientists and engineers who were planning the new mission, was to place an advanced Mariner in permanent orbit around Mars.

The events that led to the first successful placement of a spacecraft into orbit around another planet actually began in September 1968, when NASA authorized the Mariner-Mars 1971 Project with the objectives of mapping the planet and observing its dynamic characteristics over a period of 90 days. Six experiments, all of them similar to those of the 1969 Mariners, were chosen to form the science payload: television, ultraviolet spectroscopy, infrared spectroscopy, infrared radiometry, occultation, and celestial mechanics. The scientists selected by NASA formed several teams, representing the different experiments, with each team specifying the requirements of its investigation to the project scientists and engineers charged with designing the spacecraft and the mission. Eleven principal investigators, five of whom were keyed to the television experiment, were selected to represent these experiment teams in the mission-planning phase of the project, meeting with key project personnel to determine, from an almost infinite number of alternatives, the best trajectories and operating sequences.

The chosen plan specified that two identical spacecraft be launched to perform separate, but complementary, missions. The first was to be placed in an 11.98-hour orbit with an 80° inclination to the Mars equator and a periapsis (closest approach) altitude of about 1250 kilometers. This flight was intended primarily as a mapping and polar reconnaissance mission, re-turning about 5400 pictures and spectral data during the 90 days.

The second spacecraft was to be placed in a 20.5-hour orbit (five-sixths the rotational period of Mars) with a 50° inclination and 850-kilometer periapsis. The orbit period was chosen to permit repeated coverage of the same areas of Mars to study variable surface features. The 50° inclination and 850-kilometer periapsis allowed high-resolution coverage of the midlatitudes where these features could be observed to the best advantage. About 3000 pictures and spectral data were expected from this mission.

The sequencing of events for each of the two missions was carefully planned to insure that each experiment had ample opportunity to pursue its major goals. The primary objectives of the ultraviolet spectroscopy experiment were to study the composition, structure, and dynamics of the upper atmospheric regions of Mars, to measure the atmospheric surface pressure over most of the planet, and to search for localized concentrations of ozone. The instrument itself, which was much the same as that used on Mariners 6 and 7, consisted of a two-element telescope that focused ultraviolet light into a simple, rugged spectrometer, where it was dispersed into a spectrum by a diffraction grating and focused through two exit slits onto separate photomultiplier tube detectors. The cathode materials for the detectors were selected so that each was sensitive in a different bandpass of the ultraviolet, one responding in the 145- to 350-nanometer region and the other in the region from 110 to 190 nanometers. The spectral sweep through these regions was accomplished once every 3 seconds by rotating the diffraction grating.

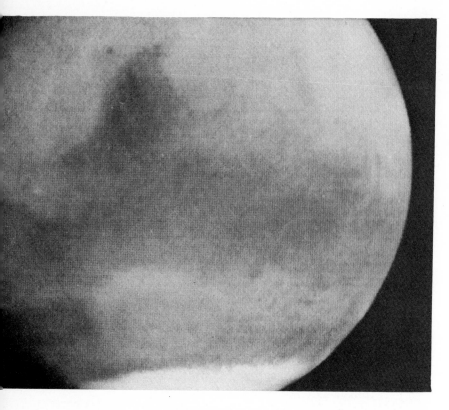

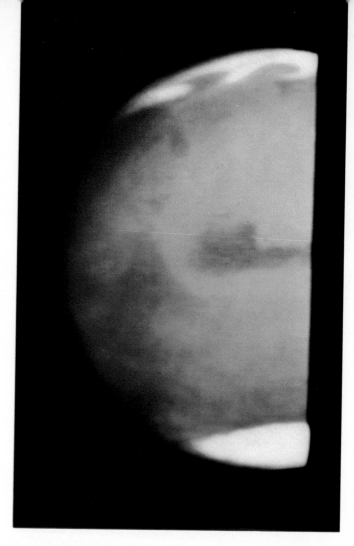

A closeup view of Syrtis Major. This photograph was taken by the Mariner 6 telephoto camera on July 29, 1969. The darkest, triangular marking is Syrtis Major; the light oval to the south is Hellas. The south polar cap is at the edge of the frame at the bottom.

A mosaic of three black-and-white views of Mars by Mariner 7 taken with different color filters in August 1971 produces this color view of a portion of the Martian disk. (Jet Propulsion Laboratory)

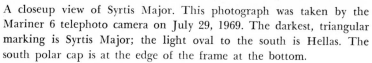

Mariner 6 wide-angle view of the cratered terrain of Mars. The region is Deucalionis Regio, photographed July 31, 1969.

Mariner 6 telephoto frame, taken July 31, 1969, showing "chaotic terrain" in lower center.

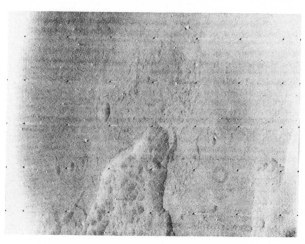

Following the Mariner 4 mission, U.S. Geological Survey artist Don Davis, consulting with J. McCauley and other Survey astrogeologists, made this painting showing craters, sand dunes, volcanic flows, and other hypothesized features of the Martian surface, based on analyses through 1969. (U.S. Geological Survey)

Like the ultraviolet spectrometer, the infrared radiometer chosen for Mariner 1971 was nearly the same as its predecessor on Mariners 6 and 7. Using refractive optics, infrared radiation was focused onto two thermopile detectors through separate filters, each covering a different wavelength band (8 to 12 and 18 to 25 micrometers). The source of radiation was alternated by a digitally stepped mirror between Mars, the 4° Kelvin background of deep space, and an internal surface of known temperature (measured by a thermistor). Martian surface temperatures could thus be derived by comparing Mars with the two sources corresponding to known temperatures. From these data, information could be gained concerning the thermal properties of the surface materials, irregularities in cooling rates, or the existence of "hot spots" indicative of internal heat sources.

Among the major goals of the infrared spectroscopy experiment were the detection and measurement of the minor constituents in the Martian atmosphere, including the total water vapor content, and the temperature of the atmosphere as a function of height. Information could also be obtained for the temperature, composition, and thermal properties of the surface similar to that obtained by the infrared radiometer experiment. The interferometer spectrometer chosen for the experiment had not previously been used on interplanetary missions, but similar instruments had been flown on Earth-orbiting Nimbus satellites. In essence, it used a beamsplitter to divide the incoming radiation into two approximately equal components that were then reflected from two mirrors, recombined at the beamsplitter, and focused on a detector. To obtain a scan containing spectral information, one reflecting mirror was moved with respect to the other, causing the two beams to travel unequal distances before recombining, and resulting in an interference pattern between the two beams as the various wavelength components went in and out of phase. This interference pattern—called an interferogram—was detected and recorded for subsequent conversion to an actual spectrum by a complicated mathematical procedure known as a Fourier transformation.

As on the previous Mariners, the S-band occultation experiment was based on analysis of the distortion of the radio signals passing through the Martian atmosphere. However, with the multiplicity of occultations provided by an orbiter, information could be obtained on the shape of the planet as well as variations in the properties of the atmosphere with latitude, season, and time of Martian day. Like the S-band occultation studies, no specific instrument was needed for the celestial mechanics experiment except the spacecraft radio. Through tracking

observations of the motions of the spacecraft, celestial mechanics information could be obtained that would help to determine the size, shape, distance, and position of Mars and to detect any large concentrations of mass (mascons) on the planet.

The two spacecraft designed to accomplish this formidable set of objectives were similar to Mariners 6 and 7, the most obvious difference being the large engines needed to place them in orbit around Mars. Like all their predecessors, they were inertially stabilized with their solar panels always facing the Sun and with their roll position controlled by a star tracker pointed at Canopus. The solar panels were designed to supply 350 to 500 watts of power to the spacecraft continuously during the missions, excepting those periods during propulsion maneuvers when the panels were turned away from the Sun and the spacecraft battery supplied power.

The experimental high-rate telemetry system, used with great success by Mariners 6 and 7, became the standard system for Mariners 8 and 9. However, it was anticipated that lower data rates would be necessary late in the missions to compensate for the loss in signal strength due to the increasing distance between Mars and Earth and the slowly degrading pointing alinement between the spacecraft's fixed antennas and the 64-meter antenna at Goldstone. Thus, in addition to the 16 200-bit-per-second rate, rates of 8100, 4050, 2025, and 1012 bits per second were designed into the Mariner 8 and 9 telemetry system.

As the design of the spacecraft and the mission proceeded, the ground-support facilities were also being designed and organized. These

Launch of Mariner 9 from Kennedy Space Center, May 30, 1971.

Mariner spacecraft being readied for launch. White shroud protects spacecraft mechanisms. Television cameras and other instruments are out of sight at the bottom. Solar panels are extended, and technicians indicate the scale of the spacecraft. (Jet Propulsion Laboratory)

Mariner spacecraft ready for flight, showing television camera and other instruments mounted on scanning platform, bottom.

Goldstone tracking antenna, which received radio signals from Mariner 9. From Goldstone the signals were relayed to viewing monitors in the Jet Propulsion Laboratory where scientists made copies and conducted analysis.

facilities included tracking systems and computer equipment to process the transmitted data. Mission planners decided to maintain an "adaptive operational capability" throughout the orbital missions—meaning that the mission plan could be changed on short notice if required by unexpected events or unanticipated discoveries. As will be seen, this adaptive mode became crucial to the success of Mariner 9.

In contrast to the modest data rates of the nonimaging experiments, the high data rate of the television cameras and the need to process the pictures rapidly on the ground made ground support for the television experiment quite formidable. Ground-support activities for television were therefore divided into two areas: termed "real-time" and "non-real-time" processing.

Real-time processing involved three versions of each incoming image for distribution to the science teams within 24 hours. Each version was produced by computer processing the television data, which were transmitted as a set of numbers representing light values for dots making up the image—as in a newspaper's Teletype photographs. The first of these, called a "shading-corrected" version, represented a first-approximation removal of camera-induced intensity gradients across the raw picture. The second was a "contrast-enhanced" version of the first, accomplished by linearly expanding the range of luminance represented by the picture—similar to increasing the contrast on a home television set. The third, a "high-pass filter" version, was designed to enhance contrast of fine details at the expense of gross contrast differences.

While many special processes were available to aid non-real-time studies by the television experimenters, the ultimate requirement for non-real-time processing, because of the mapping nature of the mission, was complete geometric correction, photometric correction, removal of errors or omissions due to the telemetry, and removal of residual ("ghost") images. These decalibrated pictures were then to be enhanced, orthographically rectified, scaled, and assembled into large maps of the Martian surface.

Early in 1971, Mariners 8 and 9 were moved from the Jet Propulsion Laboratory to the Kennedy Space Center in preparation for launch. Following a systematic sequence of events during which each spacecraft was armed, fueled, enshrouded, and mated to its launch vehicle, Mariner 8 was launched on May 9. The elation felt by those who had labored over Mariner 8 for more than 2 years as they watched it disappear, on course, into the night sky was to be short lived. A malfunction in the guidance system of the Centaur stage caused the vehicle to tumble, prematurely separating the payload and cutting off the engine. Lacking orbital velocity, Mariner 8 fell into the sea some 350 miles northwest of Puerto Rico.

That the loss of Mariner 8 did not preclude accomplishment of many Mariner objectives is a tribute not only to the concept of a backup spacecraft, but also to the project personnel who immediately set about redesigning the Mariner 9 mission to incorporate the major goals of both missions. The newly chosen orbital parameters included an 11.98-hour orbital period with a 65° inclination and a periapsis altitude of 1250 kilometers. Being 17/35 of a Martian mean solar day, the new orbital period meant that after 17 Martian days and 35 spacecraft revolutions, the track on the surface of Mars would begin to repeat itself under essentially the same solar illumination conditions, allowing areas to be restudied in a search for variable features. The minimum periapsis altitude of 1250 kilometers was chosen from mapping consideration to insure that, when two consecutive wide-angle pictures were taken looking straight down at periapsis, there would be some overlap. Any gaps between pictures taken near periapsis on successive orbits could be filled in on the subsequent 17-day cycles. The 65° orbit inclination was a compromise between the higher inclination, preferred for mapping and polar observations, and the lower inclination, which was more favorable for studying variable features and time-of-day (diurnal) effects in equatorial regions.

Mariner 9 was successfully launched on May 30, 1971, and 6 days later a trajectory correction was made so accurately that no other corrections were necessary for the entire 167-day trip to Mars. After traveling 394 million kilometers, the spacecraft arrived at the planet within 50 kilometers of the target point, a feat virtually indescribable by any earthly analogy. As Mariner 9 made this precise journey, planning for the new mission continued. The new plan was destined to be so successful that Mariner 9 would eventually achieve every objective of both former missions, returning over 7000 pictures and completely mapping the surface of Mars.

CHAPTER IV

Mars Encounter and the Great Dust Storm of 1971

Besides the permanent spots, I have often noticed occasional changes in partial bright belts. . . . [These may be due to] clouds and vapors floating in the atmosphere of the planet.
—William Herschel, approximately 1784, quoted by S. Gladstone

During prelaunch planning, it was determined that Mariner 9 would arrive at Mars during rapid shrinking of the south polar cap, when markings in the southern hemisphere would be rapidly darkening. The adaptive mission was therefore designed on the basis of anticipated early detection of interesting surface features.

However, on September 22, 1971, nearly 4 months after launch and nearly 2 months before Mars encounter, a brilliant whitish cloud appeared within a space of a few hours over the Noachis region and spread in the next days to become one of the greatest and most widespread Martian dust storms ever recorded.

The storm was first photographed in South Africa by G. Roberts at the Republic Observatory. As tracked by observers at New Mexico State University Observatory and Lowell Observatory in Flagstaff, Ariz., it spread from an initial streaklike core about 2400 kilometers in length and expanded slowly for 2 days. On September 24 the storm began to expand more rapidly, especially to the west. By September 27 a large area stretching from the east edge of Hellas west across Noachis was obscured, and the storm cloud was encroaching on Syrtis Major to the north. University of Arizona photographs on September 28 showed a new cloud develop-

ing in Eos, a region later found to be part of the great canyon of Mars. Flagstaff astronomer Peter Boyce subsequently reported that the contrast of features as far away from the storm core as Syrtis Major and Mare Cimmerium had faded in contrast in blue light some days before the dust cloud was first seen, indicating that Martian dust had been injected into the atmosphere before the discrete cloud became visible from Earth. By the end of September the contrast of markings had been reduced substantially around most of the planet.

On October 7, 16 days after the storm's onset, the principal bright cloud was still expanding to the west along the bright corridor of Hesperia, between the dark regions of Mare Cimmerium and Mare Tyrrhenum. The original cloud and isolated yellowish clouds in other areas had now coalesced almost entirely around the planet. A zone approximately 12 000 kilometers long had been obscured in only 16 days. This corresponds to an average advance rate of 30 to 40 kilometers per hour (20 to 30 miles per hour), but this speed is not necessarily that of the surface winds. Even red photographs from Earth showed virtually no detail during most of October. Prospects were dim for successful mapping following Mariner 9's encounter with Mars on November 14.

In retrospect, team members realized that a major dust storm should not have been totally unexpected. In fact, the possibility of such a storm occurring coincident with the Mariner 1971 mission was postulated by Lowell Observatory astronomer C. Capen in February 1971 be-

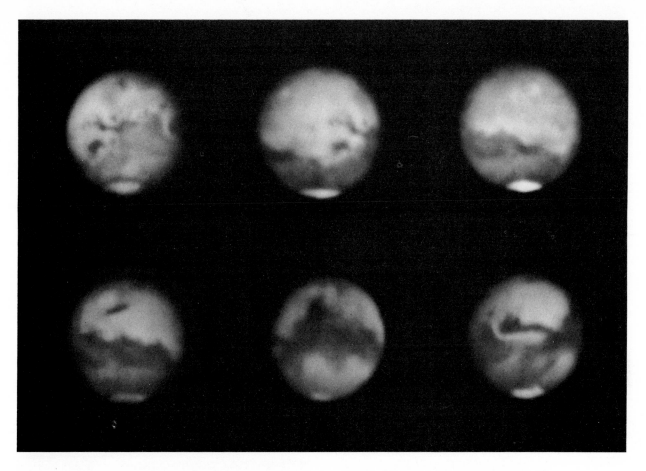

These images of Mars during summer 1971 show the clarity of its atmosphere before the great dust storm set in. From top left, dates are July 18, August 16, August 12, August 7, September 3, and August 27. (Lunar and Planetary Laboratory, University of Arizona)

The orbit of Mariner 9 between Earth and Mars.

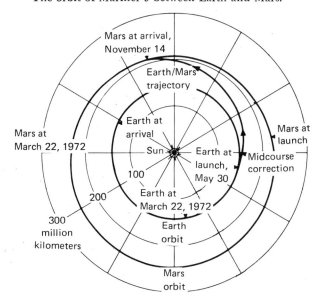

Earth-based color photograph of Mars at the height of the dust storm, showing total obscuration of all surface detail including polar cap (Lunar and Planetary Laboratory, University of Arizona)

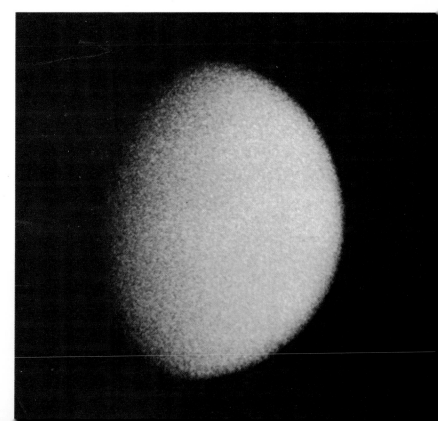

fore Mariner 9 was launched. Since 1892, during each opposition of Mars that coincided with Mars' closest approach to the Sun, terrestrial observers had noted substantial dust storms. They were noted in 1892, 1909, 1924–25, 1939, and 1956. As early as 1909, the French observer Antoniadi had pointed out that the most intense storms occurred near Mars' perihelion passage. It was later reasoned that because the radiation received from the Sun at perihelion is more than 20 percent stronger than the average radiation, the surface and lower atmosphere would be heated to substantially higher temperatures than normal, causing instabilities in the atmosphere. In arid regions on Earth, similar instabilities give rise to "dust devils"—swirling columns of air that entrain dust and debris and lift them into the air. Some theorists proposed that this might be the mechanism for lifting Martian dust and maintaining dust clouds.

Such dust clouds might be self-perpetuating by a feedback effect proposed by the Soviet meteorologist G. S. Golitsyn, who suggests that once the dust cloud is formed, its absorption of sunlight cools the surface underneath it, causing atmospheric temperature instabilities that then increase the local wind, stirring up more dust. Once the storm has spread, as long as Mars is near perihelion, any local clearing would allow more heat to reach the surface causing new atmospheric winds and restirring the surface dust. The American meteorologists P. Gierasch and R. Goody have recently published detailed calculations supporting such a model of Martian dust storms.

On November 4, Mariner 9 team members reviewed the progress of the storm and concluded that it would still obscure Mars at the time of encounter. While some experiments such as the radio-occultation experiment would not be adversely affected by the dust storm, the television experiment would be severely affected. The question was how much detail was visible on the surface. From Earth, only the polar regions were dimly visible.

On November 8, the first pictures of Mars came back from Mariner 9. These were merely calibration pictures, to test the television system. The diameter of Mars was about 25 picture elements, large enough to show some detail under normal conditions. Even the processed versions of these pictures showed no detail except for the phase. One scientist jokingly speculated

One of Mariner 9's first photographs of Mars, a far-encounter photograph made during approach to Mars on November 12–13, 1971. The three dusky spots toward the top were later revealed to be summits of enormous volcanic mountains protruding through the dust pall.

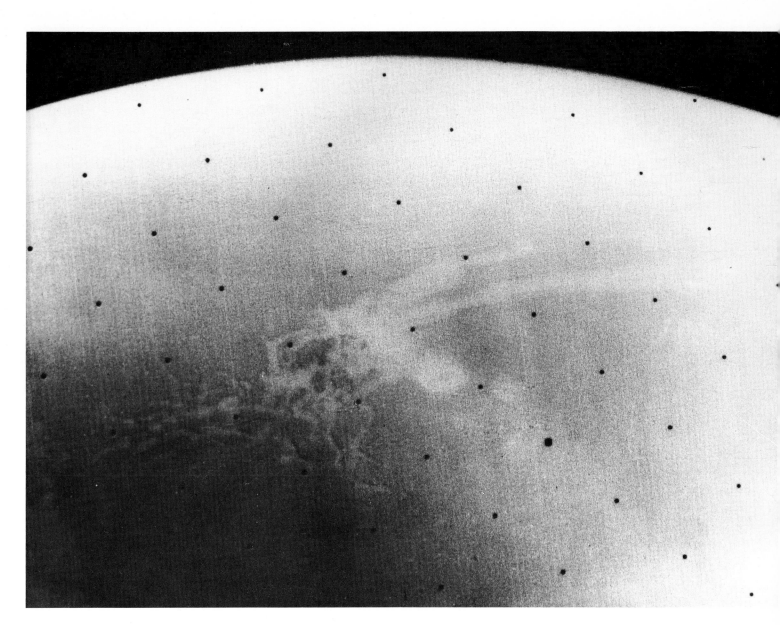

This view toward the horizon taken on December 17 shows the west end of the canyon system emerging from the dust. In the lower left, some shadows can be seen in the branching latticework of canyons. (Black dots are reseau marks allowing geometric calibration of photographs.)

Mars 3, launched by the Soviet Union on May 19 and 29, respectively. Each probe, weighing 4650 kilograms (somewhat over 10 000 pounds—nearly eight times the weight of Mariner 9), carried an orbiter and a sterilized landing package that was designed to enter the Martian atmosphere, eject its conical heat shield, and parachute a hemispherical capsule through the atmosphere to about 20 to 30 meters above the surface, where it would land with the assistance of a braking rocket. Each orbiter also contained instruments for remote sensing of Mars. Mars 2 entered a highly elliptical orbit on November 27. Its parameters were—

Orbital period . . . . 18 hours
Inclination to Mars
   equator . . . . : 48.9°

Complex crater on the summit of "north spot" volcano, renamed Ascraeus Mons, appears in this photograph taken December 17. The darkest parts of the rim are most free of dust; lower flanks of the mountain are obscured by bright dust clouds.

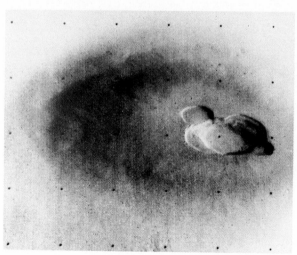

Minimum altitude
   (periapsis) . . . . 1380 kilometers
Maximum altitude
   (apoapsis) . . . . 24 900 kilometers

Just before entering orbit, Mars 2 released its capsule, which is believed to have landed about 500 kilometers southwest of Hellas, at latitude —44.2° and longitude 313.2°. Although no useful scientific information was transmitted back, this became the first manmade object to arrive on Mars. Perhaps the dust and high winds interfered with the landing procedure.

Mars 3 ejected its lander and entered an even more elliptical orbit 5 days later on December 2. The orbit parameters were—

Orbital period . . . . 12 days, 16 hours
Inclination to equator . . 60°
Minimum altitude
   (periapsis) . . . . 1530 kilometers
Maximum altitude
   (apoapsis) . . . . 190 000 kilometers

The Mars 3 lander successfully landed on Mars and within 1½ minutes was activated by its time sequencer. It began to transmit a television picture of the Martian surface to the orbiter, which would relay the picture to Earth. After 20 seconds—having transmitted only part of one frame—it suddenly ceased transmitting. In spite of intensive attempts to process this fractional frame of the Martian surface, no recognizable detail has been found by Soviet analysts. It may be that a picture of a Martian dust storm is indeed a featureless gray frame!

Various hypotheses have been suggested to explain why the Mars 3 lander stopped transmitting. Did it get covered with dust, or did the

Artist's conception of swirling dust being raised during the early phases of a Martian dust storm. Artist Ludek Pesek collaborated with some members of the Mariner 9 team during preparation of this 1972 Mars painting for the National Geographic. (Painting by Ludek Pesek, © 1973, National Geographic Society)

parachute (which was supposed to jet out of the way) come down on top of the lander? Was it damaged on impact, even though it was designed to withstand a 200-mile-per-hour crash? If the suggestion of extremely high wind velocities during the dust storm is correct, it seems plausible that the lander may have been blown over, or been damaged by blowing dust. According to Soviet scientists, there was no possibility that the parachute landed on top of the lander. They verified that it landed slowly at least in the vertical velocity component, and postulated that the two most likely failure modes were an uncompensated high horizontal velocity or sinkage through Martian quicksand. The Mars 3 lander presumably still lies near its landing site at latitude −45° and longitude 158°,

Bright clouds lying in faulted valleys of the Valles Marineris canyon complex. The crests of the cliffs bordering the valley can barely be discerned at the edges of the bright dust clouds. (Mariner 9 telephoto view taken December 19.)

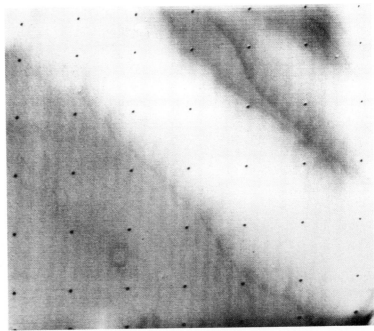

On March 1, 1972, even after most of the dust storm had cleared, bands of haze could be seen lying along the curving Martian horizon.

in a moderately light region between Electris and Phaethontis, not far from the northern limit of the southern polar cap. Perhaps one day, like Surveyor 3, these pioneering devices will be recovered and returned to Earth for placement in some future museum.

The Soviet scientists later reported that because Mariner 9 was designed to do extensive orbital imagery and mapping, their orbiters were designed to emphasize nonimaging experiments, such as infrared and ultraviolet sensing, magnetometry, and microwave radiometry. Their orbiters did carry limited imaging equipment as well, but were not designed to carry out imaging over a long time duration; hence they did not acquire significant imagery after the dust storm settled. Conceivably, had it not

been for the dust storm, we would now have photographs from the Martian surface, additional surface analysis, and more useful material from orbit.

On the other hand, the storm was in many ways a blessing in disguise. It gave scientists a chance to study not only the "normal" Mars but also the unusual storm environment. Measurements made by ultraviolet, infrared, and other instruments revealed a number of characteristics of the dust storm. Dust was stirred to heights greater than 30 kilometers (97 000 feet) above the surface during midstorm. The particles causing measured effects ranged in size from roughly 2 to 15 micrometers in diameter. Experimenters using the infrared interferometer spectrometer concluded from spectral features that the dust had a relatively high silicon content, about 60 percent, indicating that substantial geochemical differentiation has occurred on Mars. This would indicate that the interior of Mars has at least partially melted, a conclusion consistent with the presence of large volcanoes. Television experimenters noted several examples of localized dust storms during the general clearing after the main storm. One incident appeared to have been initiated by rapid southern movement of cold air following a cold front identified by characteristic cloud patterns. In these localized storms, dust was rapidly carried to heights of 15 to 20 kilometers, indicating strong convective motion of the air, probably triggered by the warming of dusty air masses due to absorption of sunlight.

CHAPTER V

The Classical Markings: Toward an Explanation

Why are the maria shaped and oriented as they are?

The absence of appreciable liquid water greatly simplifies the problem. . . . The chief agent of erosion, in all probability, is windblown sand. And winds are the chief, practically the only, agent for transportation and sedimentation.

—DEAN B. McLAUGHLIN, 1954

If we agree with [Öpik's 1950 suggestion that the maria must be continually renewed], then the problem is reduced to the identification of the formative activity.

—DEAN B. McLAUGHLIN, 1955

Once the dust storm cleared and the normal mapping of the planet began, a natural early question concerned the nature of the light and the dark markings seen by Earth-based observers. Years of telescopic observation had produced no satisfactory identification of the dark material, with hypotheses ranging from substantial vegetation through lichen-spotted lava outcrops to windblown deposits of volcanic ash. Mariners 6 and 7 in 1969 had shown the markings clearly in global far-encounter photographs, but detailed high-resolution frames with resolution down to 4 kilometers had produced no firm diagnostic information as to their ultimate cause. Instead, puzzling "chaotic terrain" and cratered areas seemed to cross the boundaries of classical dark markings, suggesting that the markings were not correlated with underlying geologic structure. Mariners 6 and 7 also showed small dark patches in some craters, but with resolution insufficient to distinguish crater-floor lava flows—such as appear in lunar craters—from aeolian deposits or vegetation patches. The markings, as possible candidates for vegetated areas, thus remained the most exciting Martian mystery.

Because of the dust storm, Mariner 9's pre-orbital far-encounter photographs did not yield global views of the dark markings. Very late in the mission, a few composite pictures of most of the disk of Mars were made from apoapsis (the farthest point of the orbit from the planet), but, unfortunately, several of these happen to show the hemisphere most devoid of dark markings. Therefore little opportunity exists to compare Earth-based and space observations of maria, oases, "canals," and large-scale changes that might appear following a major dust storm.

Thus the frames from the normal mapping sequences and certain specially targeted high-resolution pictures of dark spots are the best Mariner 9 data concerning the classical Martian markings. Much of the computer processing that has been applied so far to these photographs has not been ideal for emphasizing the kind of broad, dusky shadings found on classical Earth-based maps, however. Thus it is important to consider the nature of the processing before studying the markings. The processing usually applied is designed to emphasize small-scale detail, such as fractures, crater-rim shadows, and surface texture in different geologic provinces. This processing is analogous to a process of photographic printing in which very-high-contrast printing paper is used, with "dodg-

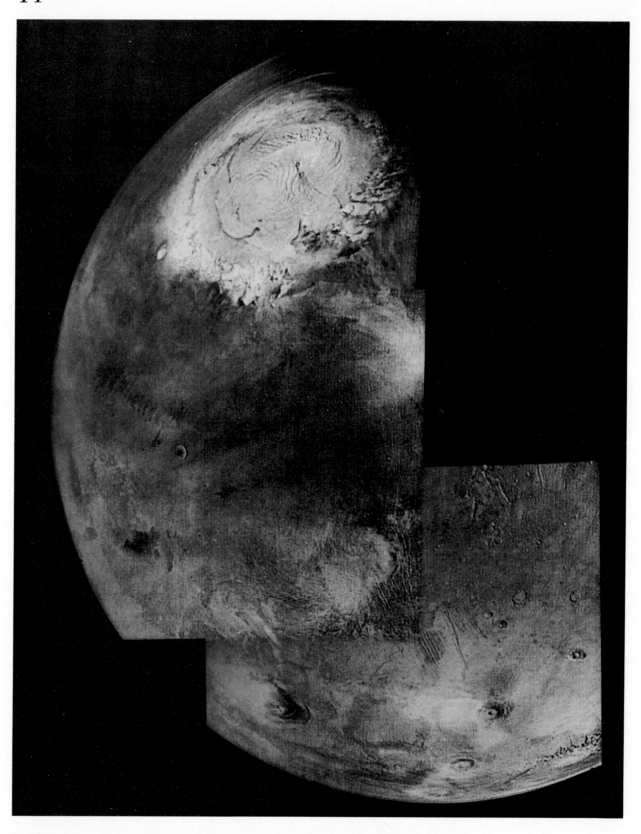

Much of the northern hemisphere of Mars is shown in this composite of several Mariner
9 frames taken late in the mission. Although the polar cap (*top*) and several volcanoes
(*bottom*) can be seen, this global view does not reveal the nature of the dark markings.

ing" applied to reduce large-scale regional contrast; the resulting print shows very high contrast among small details but may not show the original high contrast between dark and light land regions, or the rapid falloff of sunlight toward the sunrise or sunset line. For this reason, and because of variations in original exposures on the spacecraft, care must be taken in comparing different Mariner frames, because the processed images tend to have the same general background tonality, regardless of whether the original frame showed a dark region, a lighter "desert," or the intensely bright polar cap.

Because the mapping frames each cover only a very small region of Mars, their best application to the study of the large-scale markings is through mosaics of wide-angle A camera frames. Such mosaics have been prepared by the Jet Propulsion Laboratory. These include computer-produced mosaics, handmade mosaics of selected regions, and a mosaic on a 5-foot-diameter globe, covering the whole planet. At the same time, the U.S. Geological Survey Center for Astrogeology and Lowell Observatory have produced a number of airbrush renderings of physical structure and classical markings based on the Mariner 9 mapping.

In addition to these methods for enhancing large-scale markings, special processing was carried out by Stanford University's Artificial Intelligence Laboratory and by the Jet Propulsion Laboratory. These processes included rectification (computerized reprocessing of pictures to remove effects of oblique viewing angle), calibration of intensities on different photographs, and differencing (a technique of comparing pic-

Streaks within Syrtis Major, near 283°, +13°. (1409–211522)

tures to detect any changes from one frame to a later frame).

What can be learned from these materials about the cause of the classical markings of Mars? The Mariner A camera photographs and mosaics have too low a resolution to solve the puzzle of their origin, but they give intriguing clues. One of the most interesting examples is the region of Syrtis Major—the first dark marking ever recorded on Mars by human observers. Syrtis Major is now resolved not into a single dark patch, but into a series of dark streaks, similar to streaks photographed in other areas of Mars. Almost every streak emanates from a small cra-

(Continued on page 49)

Patchy dark markings on Mars. Red, green, and blue filter photographs are combined to give this color view of the surface. Precise color reconstruction is difficult because of differences in lighting and viewing geometry between the original frames. (Jet Propulsion Laboratory)

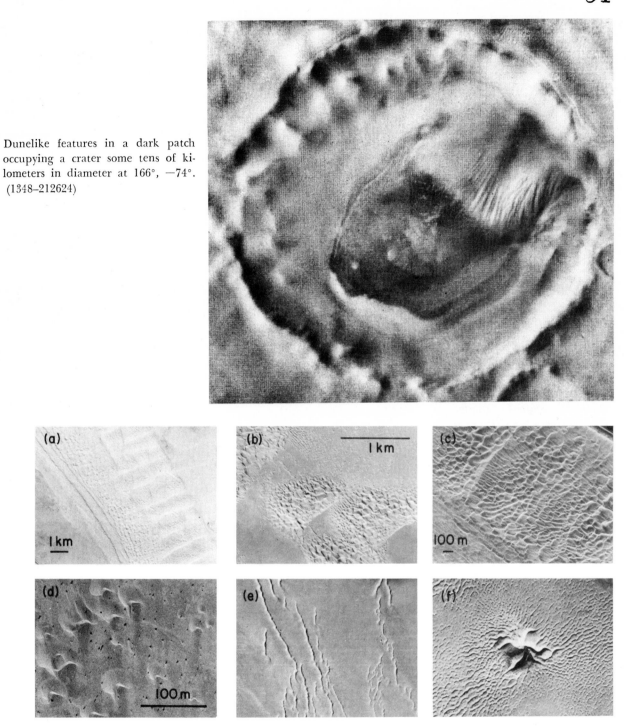

Dunelike features in a dark patch occupying a crater some tens of kilometers in diameter at 166°, −74°. (1348–212624)

Examples of terrestrial dunes. (*a–d*) Increasing resolution in the Algodones dunes of southern California. The low-resolution view (*a*) has several times better resolution than the Mariner 9 telephoto views. (*e–f*) Ridge and pyramid dune forms in the Sahara. (U.S. Air Force, R. S. U. Smith, and H. T. U. Smith)

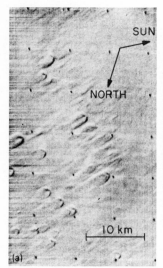

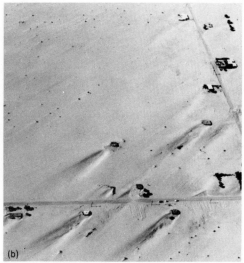

Illustration (*a*) shows the lighting and scale of the Amazonis-Memnonia elongated depressions, and (*b*) shows a much smaller example of similar features in the Coachella Valley of southern California, where houses and other buildings have produced wind shadows and elongated depressions in windblown sand. (4254–55 and J. F. McCauley, U.S. Geological Survey)

Field of bright streaks, each emanating from a crater in the Hesperia region at 241°, −23°. (4155–84)

Field of bright streaks traversing faulted terrain in southern Tharsis near 108°, −9°. Unlike most streaks, these do not emanate from craters; many appear to emanate from small irregularities on the crests of faulted cliffs. (1348–225134)

Ragged edges among terrestrial sand deposits caused by fluted cliffs and windblown deposits. High-altitude view over central Peru. (U.S. Geological Survey)

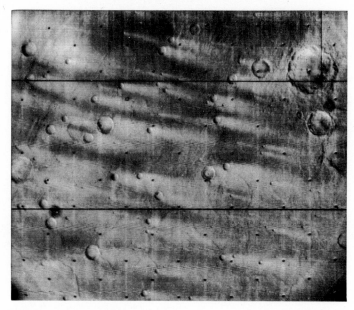

Artist's conception of a dark streak or "tail" emanating from a distant obstacle that interrupts the wind flow. The streak is interpreted by the artist as an alinement of dunes. (Don Davis, Morrison Planetarium)

Streaks and patches in a region, about 500 kilometers top to bottom, corresponding to the position of the "canal" Hiddekel, near 348°, +9°. The northeast-southwest orientation of the streaks approximates that of the "canal" as shown on old maps, but it is uncertain whether the area, photographed shortly after the 1971 dust storm, has the same appearance that it presented to Lowell, Schiaparelli, and other early observers. (4168–72)

Simulation of Martian windblown streaks near craters in wind tunnel tests at Ames Research Center, NASA. Photographs *D* and *H* are of Martian craters. Additional photographs are of wind tunnel test models showing evolution as sand is blown across the crater. Photographs *C* and *G* show simulations of the Martian observed features.

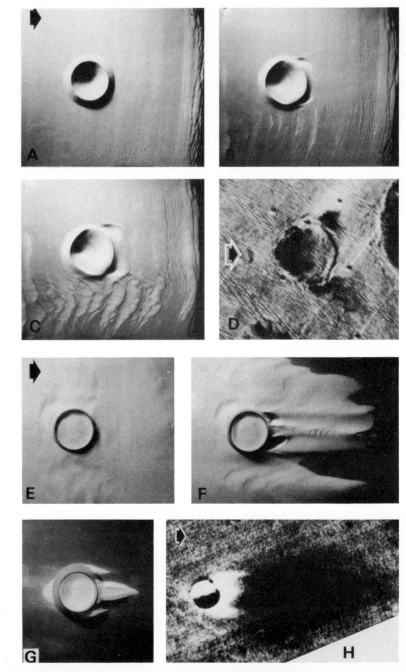

was found that the observed streaks and accumulated deposits on crater floors and on leeward rims can be reproduced vividly. This work again supports the assertion that the streaks, splotches, and dune fields are depositions or scourings of dust.

These discoveries provide only a general kind of solution to the mystery of the Martian markings: they are related to, or a product of, deposition of fine material carried about by high winds, especially the winds that produce the major dust storms. Thus Mariner 9 has provided much of the solution—or perhaps the entire solution—to the mystery of the Martian markings. This solution accounts for the changes in the markings observed from Earth from year to year, because the patterns are expected to change as the winds shift. At the same time, it accounts for the long-term stability of the markings, because Mars, as Earth, probably has relatively stable patterns of prevailing winds. These assertions are supported by the preliminary evidence, which suggests correlations between the sites of dark streaks and the orientation of local steep slopes with respect to the local wind direction.

A number of specifics of the problem are not yet solved, however. For example, not only dark streaks but also light streaks have been revealed by Mariner 9. These follow a pattern similar to the dark streaks, emanating from craters, but raise the necessity of accounting for both dark and light materials. Mariner 9 photographs showed many instances of dark streaks and patches changing shape, but no instance where bright streaks change. However, new bright streaks appeared in the 2-year interval between Mariner 6 and 7 and Mariner 9 photographs.

One hypothesis concerning these facts is that Martian materials are sorted by particle size. (It is well known that fine powders of rock material are usually lighter in tone than coarse powders or the unpowdered rock itself.) According to this hypothesis, the dark and bright markings of Mars might not be much different in mineralogy, only different in mean particle size, and whether local streaks or splotches were darker or lighter than the background would depend on whether the deposited particles were finer or coarser than the background. As Sagan and Pollack noted in 1969, the physics of windblown dust on Mars dictates that winds of a certain minimum speed are required to lift any particles, but still higher winds will lift both finer and coarser particles as well. The fines might be responsible for the light streaks, which change only rarely because the necessary high-speed winds are rare.

This particle-size hypothesis is difficult to prove, however, in view of rather crude evidence of differences in the spectroscopic and radar tests of the dark and bright markings. These differences, particularly in color and spectral absorption characteristics, could be due to mineralogical differences. Such a suggestion is consistent with the Mariner 9 infrared spectroscopic indications that Mars has undergone at least partial melting and differentiation into silica-rich and silica-poor rocks. The former are usually lighter in color and the latter, darker. Similar differentiation has occurred to varying degrees on Earth and the Moon. Thus, might Martian markings result from uneven distribution of light (silica-rich) and dark (silica-poor) rock powders.

(Continued on page 63)

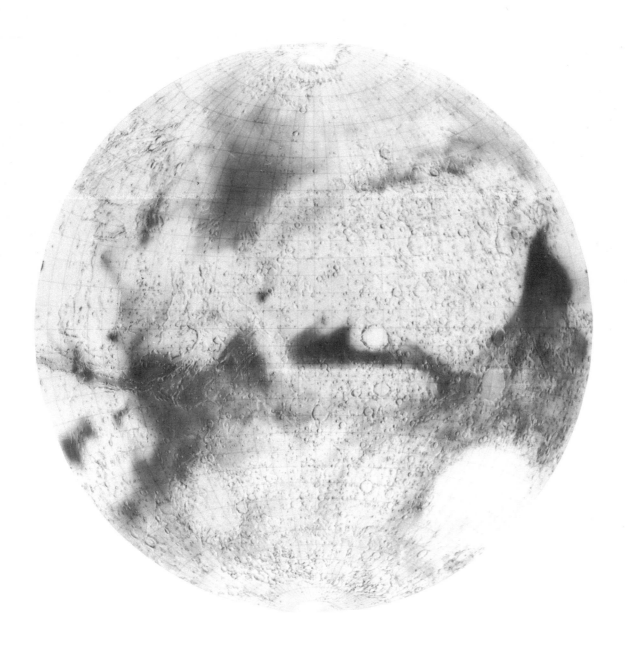

Airbrush drawings of three faces of Mars, showing the classical markings superimposed on physical relief detected by Mariner 9, appear on this and the following two pages. No high degree of correlation is found between markings and terrain type. Compare with earlier maps in this book. (Lowell Observatory)

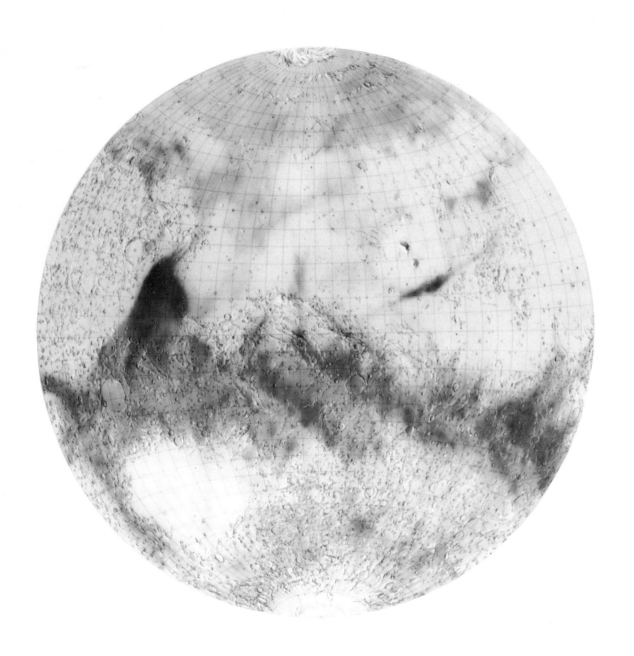

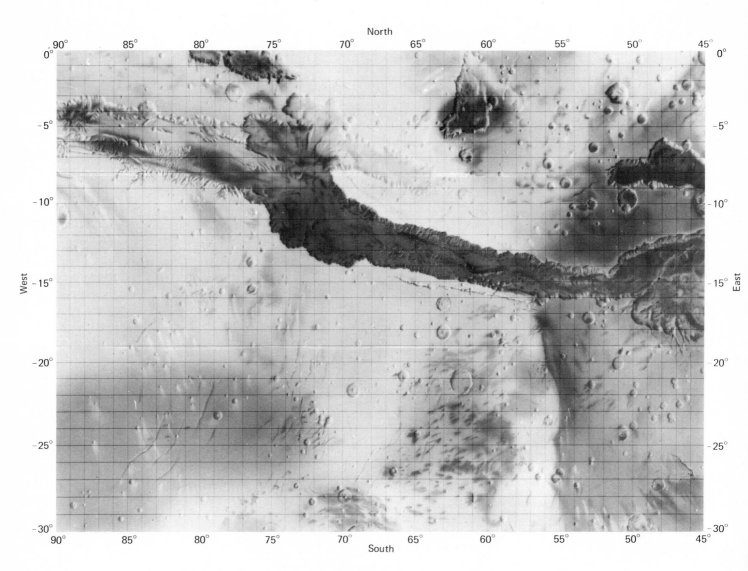

North

South

West

East

Airbrush map of Coprates area showing classical dark "canal." This dark feature coincides with the recently discovered canyon called Coprates Chasma. (James Roth and G. de Vaucouleurs, University of Texas)

August 4, 1969   January 8, 1972

The search for changes in Martian markings. Here, a frame from Mariner 7 in 1969 is compared with the same region shown in a mosaic of Mariner 9 frames. Several dark spots and streaks have developed in the intervening 2½ years.

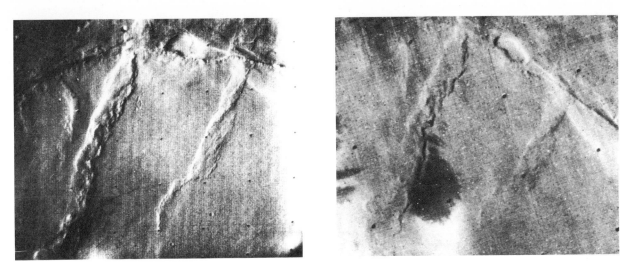

Detection of changes on the surface of Mars. This pair of Mariner 9 telephoto pictures shows the summit of the volcano Pavonis Mons on two occasions 77 days apart. Most of the development of the large dark spot east of the ridge occurred in a 20-day period between orbits 154 and 195 of Mariner 9. The hypothesis of deposition of windblown dust, which accounts for variations in many dark patches, has been questioned in this case because of the high altitude and low atmospheric pressure at this location. (4096–80, 4267–42)

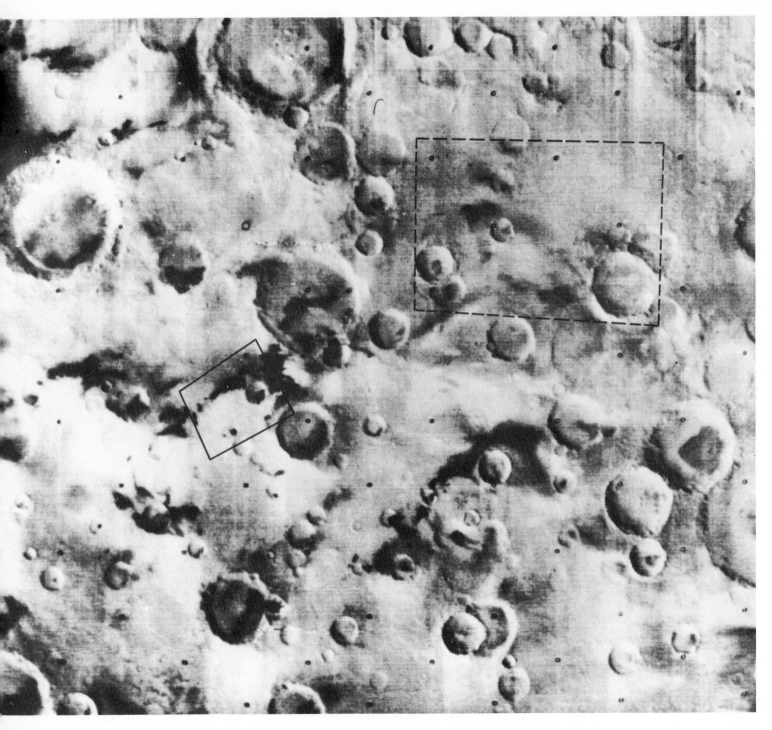

Region in Promethei Sinus (269°, −71°) where variable dark patches were noted by Mariner analysts. This wide-angle view covers an area about 750 kilometers across. Boxes show areas studied in detail; variable features in the small box are shown in the next picture. (4211–9)

Telephoto view of variable features in Promethei Sinus, centered at 253°, −70°. Features lettered *A* to *F* have ragged edges, characteristic of windblown deposits. Feature *A* was observed to change shape dramatically, as shown below. (Photograph width is about 80 kilometers.)

Changes on Mars. The spade-shaped marking developed between the taking of the left and middle photographs. The marking is *A* in the above picture. This sequence shows a technique for detecting and portraying changes developed at Stanford's Artificial Intelligence Laboratory. The differences in brightness between elements of the left and middle pictures are displayed at the right. Regions where no change has occurred are neutral gray; regions of variation appear bright or dark. (Stanford University)

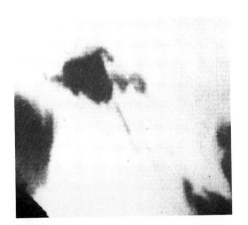

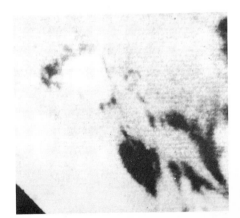

Low-altitude aerial view of terrestrial dunes and windblown deposits in northwest Mexico showing ragged forms developed by interaction with local topography of different reflectivity. (W. Hartmann)

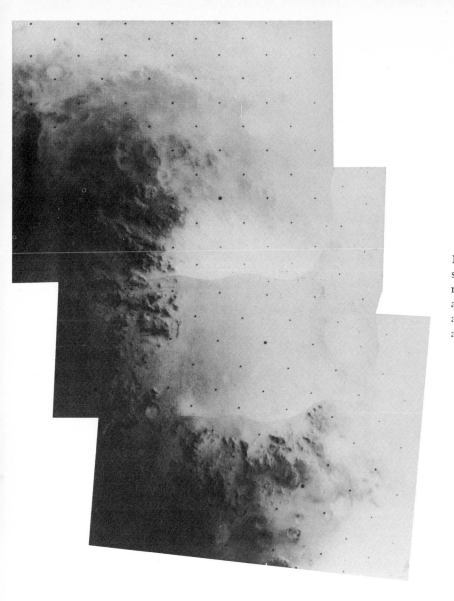

Mosaic of photographs showing the Argyre I basin. These show the original light and dark tones, with sunlight from the right (east), and washed-out detail in regions of high lighting angle as well as in the basin interior where there is probably airborne dust. Argyre I has long been noted on Earth-based maps as a bright spot roughly 1000 kilometers in diameter.

Region of Moeris Lacus basin (right of center, featureless circular floor) and Syrtis Major (left of center, dark streaks). The most prominent streaks in Syrtis Major correspond to the rim and wall structure of the Moeris Lacus basin, perhaps being initiated by topography in that region.

Edom, long observed as a bright spot on Earth-based maps, is here resolved into a large shallow crater occupying the central third of this mosaic. The crater has been named Schiaparelli, after the famous observer of Mars. The dark markings at the left are part of the eastern "prong" of the fork-shaped Meridiani Sinus.

This 185-kilometer-diameter crater on Mars shows an inner ring of peaks and concentric ridge structure on its rim. Beyond the rim are radial striations. Such a structure is believed to be produced by the mechanics of the impact process when large meteorites strike planetary surfaces. The crater resembles a similar structure on the Moon, named Schrödinger, discovered in the late 1960's in Lunar Orbiter photography. (406–192722)

Martian crater near 260°, +38° with well-formed central peak and radially striated ejecta blanket. The hummocky exterior ejecta blanket is believed to be a deposit of fragmental material thrown out of the crater during its formation. (1433–210033)

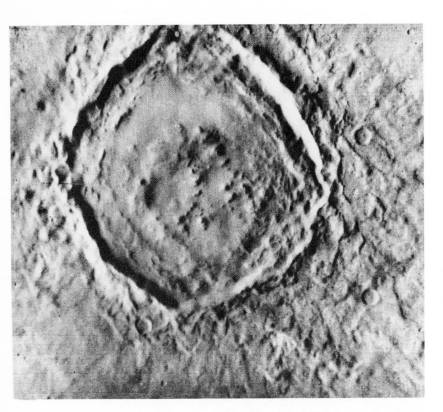

Martian crater near 330°, +30° displaying central hills and hummocky radial outer rim structure. (1419–153055)

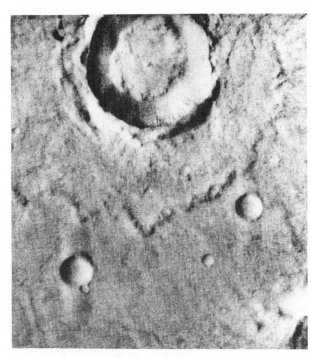

Example of a possibly exhumed ejecta blanket surrounding a crater. Instead of feathering out into the surroundings as is normal, this ejecta blanket appears to stand out above the surroundings, possibly as a result of erosion of surrounding loose material. (1590–121733)

eastern and northern edges grading out into a broad expanse of Martian "desert."

Although these basins are the only craterlike features large enough to be distinguished (but not identified) from Earth, certain smaller craters apparently affect the pattern of markings sufficiently that their immediate regions were given names by pre-Mariner telescopic observers. Two of these craters, each about 470 kilometers (290 miles) in diameter, occupy the regions of Iapygia and Edom. Iapygia was shown on Flammarion's map as long ago as

1909 as a circular spot slightly brighter than its dark background (just south of Syrtis Major) and coinciding with what we now know to be the crater floor. Edom has long been recorded by telescopic observers as one of the brightest desert patches, just east of the forked bay of Meridiani Sinus. By extension of the evidence for dust clouds in Hellas, one suspects that these craters may be the sites of dust deposits stirred by winds, creating brighter-than-background clouds recorded by Earth-based observers. Old maps show numerous such bright

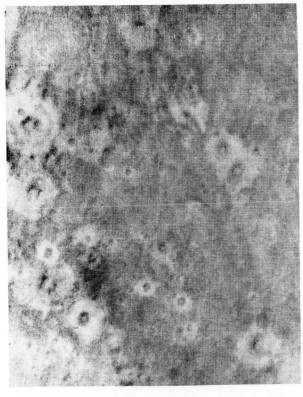

Unusual pattern of bright ejecta blankets surrounding craters near 31°, +60°. The explanation might involve ejection of underlying light material on dark surface material, or possible deposition of frost or other light material on rough ejecta blanket surfaces. (7270–195648)

A highly eroded Martian crater near 325°, +37° with a sinuous arroyolike channel winding across its floor. This and similar craters testify to various processes smoothing, eroding, and obliterating the ancient craters on Mars. (1419–154957)

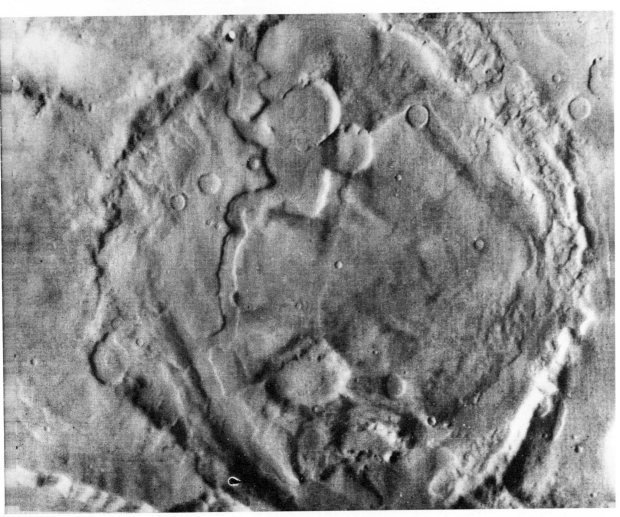

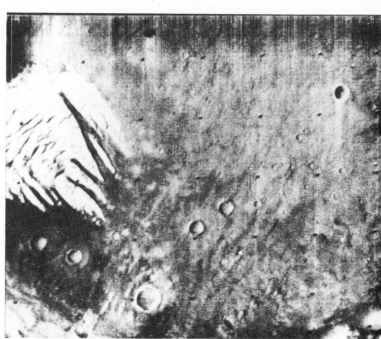

Enigmatic bright formation in a Martian crater. The wide-angle frame (*left*) shows the location of the feature in the floor of a crater at top edge, center. The telephoto view (*right*) shows the bright structure at the left edge of the frame. The feature resembles a windblown bright deposit with ragged edges, but it is of unusually high reflectivity.

patches, which may represent dust activity in craters.

Do the myriad of smaller craters on Mars have any bearing on the markings seen from Earth? Mariner 9 photographs showed that many craters display dark patches deposited on their floors. In general, such dark patches are too small to be resolved from Earth, but it is of interest to recall that late pre-Mariner French observers such as Lyot, Focas, and Dollfus, observing visually under excellent conditions with resolutions corresponding to as little as 56 kilometers (35 miles) on Mars (under full-disk illumination), stated that the dark markings were composed of "innumerable small spots" (Dollfus) or "dark nuclei" (Focas). Because the craters appear in the bright areas of Arabia and Moab as well as in dark areas, one cannot ascribe all of the classical dark markings to crater effects alone, but a case can be made from the association of the dark areas and craters that the craters do influence the markings seen from Earth.

The smallest craters so far resolved on Mars by Mariner 9 measure some hundreds of meters in diameter, and there is every reason to believe that still smaller examples exist. However, craters as small as a few kilometers and less

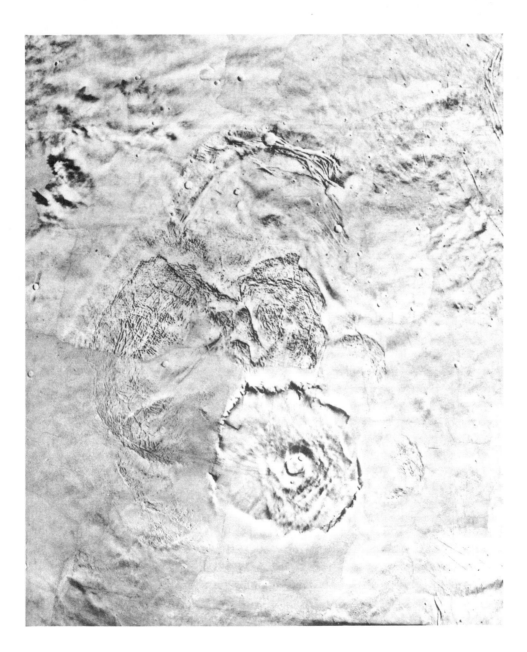

Mosaic of Mariner 9 photographs showing Olympus Mons and the nearby fractured or "grooved" terrain. (Jet Propulsion Laboratory)

base is about as big as the whole State of Missouri, towered some 88 000 feet above other features on Mars, compared with Mount Everest's 29 000 feet above sea level, 42 000 feet above the mean ocean floor, and 65 000 feet above the greatest ocean depths. At first, many analysts believed that there must be some calibration error in the ultraviolet spectroscopy data. However, recent analyses by various other techniques, such as photogrammetry, converge on a height of about 24 kilometers, or about 78 000 feet above the 6.1-millibar reference level. This puts the summit of Olympus Mons about 100 000 feet higher than the lowest places on Mars. Mars thus has about half again the total 65 000-foot relief of Earth.

Nix Olympica, as it turned out, had been aptly named. When Schiaparelli back in 1877 named this small dark spot, he was struck by its frequent transformation into a bright, cloud-like patch. Perhaps conceiving it as a sometimes snow-covered peak, he named it "Nix Olympica," meaning "snows of Olympus." So the highest mountain on Mars is associated with the home of the Greek gods. Because the classical names apply in principle only to the bright and dark patches seen from Earth, the actual volcanic peaks received their own new names from a committee of the International Astronomical Union in 1973; the mountain near Nix Olympica was thus named Olympus Mons.

How has the mountain reached such a height? Most of the height is due to the buildup of repeated outpourings of lava, as evidenced by the flows descending the conical slopes away from the summit caldera. Part of the elevation of the lower reaches may be due to uplifted, fractured blocks because such fractured blocks are exposed on the lip of the cliffs defining the edge of Olympus Mons. In addition, the whole mountain is sitting on the summit of a broad uplifted dome or ridge known on classical maps as the Tharsis area and distinguished on Mariner 9 photographs by radiating fractures. The Tharsis dome is about 2500 kilometers in diameter and stands about 4 to 8 kilometers above the Martian reference level of 6.1-millibar atmospheric pressure. Thus, about one-sixth to one-third of the 24 kilometers of the summit altitude of Olympus Mons is due to very broad crustal deformation.

Olympus Mons and the other major nearby volcanoes on the Tharsis dome have been compared by Mariner 9 geologists with large volcanoes on Earth. They resemble a type of structure known as a shield volcano. A typical shield volcano on Earth is Mauna Loa in Hawaii, which is approximately 120 kilometers in diameter at its sea-floor base, has a cluster of summit calderas ranging up to several kilometers in diameter, and stands about 9 kilometers above the sea floor. The Martian shield volcanoes reach much larger sizes. Small examples on the Tharsis dome include shields 180 to 200 kilometers across with large central craters up to 60 kilometers in diameter. The three large volcanoes that accompanied Olympus Mons in protruding above the 1971 dust storm average about 400 kilometers in diameter. The middle of these stands about 11 kilometers above the surrounding plains of the Tharsis dome according to ultraviolet spectroscopy measurements. Geologic analysis reveals an aureole of fractured terrain surrounding Olympus Mons as far as

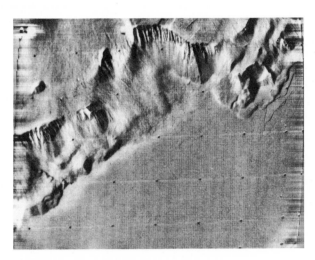

Telephoto view of the face of the cliff around the base of Olympus Mons volcano. (4265–44)

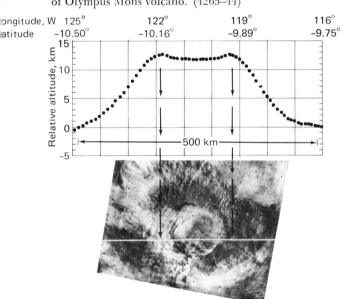

Example of a preliminary altitude profile derived for the volcano Arsia Mons from infrared radiometer measurements using thermal data and simplifying assumptions to derive local slopes. Uncertainty on the vertical scale is 50 percent.

Mariner 9 mosaic showing the volcano Ascraeus Mons (bottom) and associated fractured or "grooved" terrain. (Jet Propulsion Laboratory globe)

1400 kilometers from the center. The summit calderas of Olympus Mons, Ascraeus Mons, Pavonis Mons, and Arsia Mons are, respectively, about 65, 50, 45, and 140 kilometers in diameter.

One possible explanation of the unusually large size of the Martian volcanoes reflects on recent geological theory about Earth. On Earth, it has been established that "plates," or discrete units in the crust, move with respect to each other, giving rise to the phenomenon known as continental drift. The Hawaiian Islands, for example, are believed to have been sliding over a "hot spot," or ascending hot plume in Earth's mantle, which provides the source of the volcanic lavas. Thus instead of producing one enormous Olympus Mons-sized volcano in the central Pacific, this plume produced the string of Hawaiian Islands and a string of still older extinct volcanoes and islands extending to the northwest from Hawaii. The explanation of the Martian volcanoes, according to this hypothesis, is that the Martian crust is not as active as Earth's, lacks significant motion among its crustal units, and hence allows a volcano to reside over a given magma source long enough for an enormous volcanic pile to accumulate. Supporting evidence for this idea would help to confirm the plate tectonic model of Earth's crust. This is one example of how the exploration of Mars by Mariner 9 has begun to illuminate large-scale problems of geology on Earth.

The association of the most prominent Martian volcanoes with the broad, domed Tharsis area prompts the search for other such associations. One other clear example is found in the region of Elysium, a circular, bright area about 1800 kilometers in diameter. This area was discovered to be a broad dome by radar altimetry studies from Earth in the midsixties. Ultraviolet spectroscopy altimetry from Mariner 9 confirms that the dome rises about 3 to 5 kilometers above its surroundings. Mariner 9 photographs reveal large volcanic cones on its summit. Hence the association of Martian volcanoes and broad domes is not a random one.

Other Martian volcanoes are scattered around the planet. One example occupies a relatively uncratered plain in the midst of the cratered terrain. Because of a set of radiating ridges that reach out petallike as far as 200 kilometers from the center, this volcano earned the nickname "dandelion." Its 15-kilometer central caldera is surrounded by a ring fracture about 45 kilometers in diameter and is connected by a channel to a similar-sized depression 35 kilometers to the southwest.

Surrounding most volcanic mountains of Mars are sparsely cratered plains that, as photographed with the high-resolution B camera, reveal the telltale characteristics of lava flows. These include flowfront scarps and lobate outlines, the same characteristics that allowed identification of the lava flows on the lunar mare plains prior to the Apollo landings.

The fact that the volcanoes, domed areas, and lava flows on Mars are sparsely cratered indicates that they are considerably younger than the more heavily cratered parts of Mars. If we knew exactly how many impact craters form per century in a square kilometer on Mars, we could date these structures. Only rough estimates of the cratering rates are now available, however. Mariner 9 analysts have suggested that these

Summit caldera in Kilauea volcano, in Hawaii, showing multiple fractures and smaller collapse pits analogous to those found in the Olympus Mons caldera. (U.S. Geological Survey)

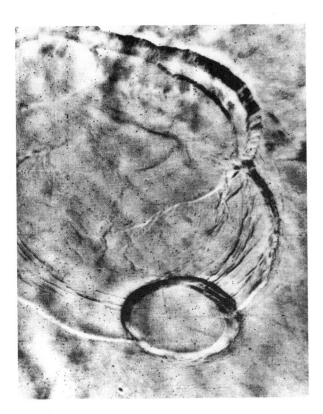

Summit caldera in the volcano Olympus Mons showing multiple fractures. (1406–164237)

Summit of shield volcano in central Elysium dome showing summit caldera, radial lava channels, and fine striations from lava flows on flanks. (4298–39)

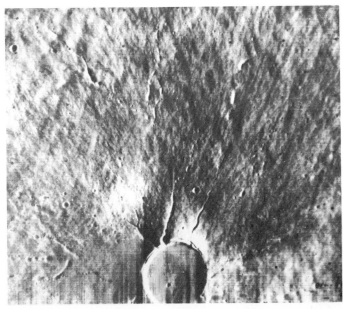

Volcanic pits on the surface of the domed volcano in the Elysium complex (210°, +31°) showing the 9-kilometer multiple-collapse caldera, radiating grooves, and crater chains. (4292–59)

Wide-angle (*left*) and telephoto (*right*) views of the flanks of Olympus Mons, showing the striated surface of the volcano. Arrows on lower picture show two long narrow lava flows running downslope, parallel to a narrow fissure. The width of the lower frame is about 55 kilometers. (Telephoto, 4133–96)

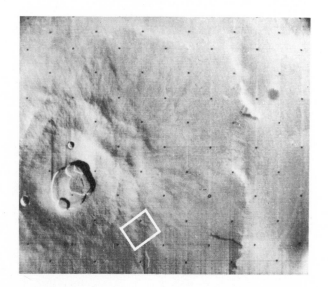

Ridges associated with summit caldera on the volcano Pavonis Mons. The telephoto view to the right shows the sinuous structure of the ridges, which resemble sites of extruded lavas found on the Moon.

units can be dated in terms of hundreds of millions of years—about a tenth the age of the planet—and that the shield volcanoes such as Nix Olympica are the youngest of the structures. Some analysts have suggested that Mars is becoming more active, and has perhaps only in the geologically recent past heated up to a point promoting active volcanism.

Another type of structure associated with the volcanoes, domed areas, and lava flows is a pattern of fractures, faults, and other disturbances of the crust. Such tectonic structures form a vast radial pattern of fractures centered on the Tharsis volcanic dome and covering about a third of the planet. These radially alined fractures show an unusual degree of symmetry for a global phenomenon, and they point accusingly back to the center of focus of the disturbance that caused them. Because their center lies at the central highest point of the Tharsis dome, they strongly suggest that the same forces responsible for the uplift were responsible for shattering the crust in a radial pattern. Mars provides a second smaller example in the Elysium volcanic dome, which is also surrounded by a radial fracture pattern.

Among the radial fractures associated with Martian volcanic domes, by far the most spectacular is the set forming the great Coprates canyon complex, recently renamed the Valles Marineris. Prior to the Mariner 9 mission, Coprates was a name associated with an unremarkable, stubby, canal-like dark marking extending from the very dark patch Aurorae Sinus and forming one border of the "eye of Mars," the Solis Lacus region. (See maps in ch. II.)

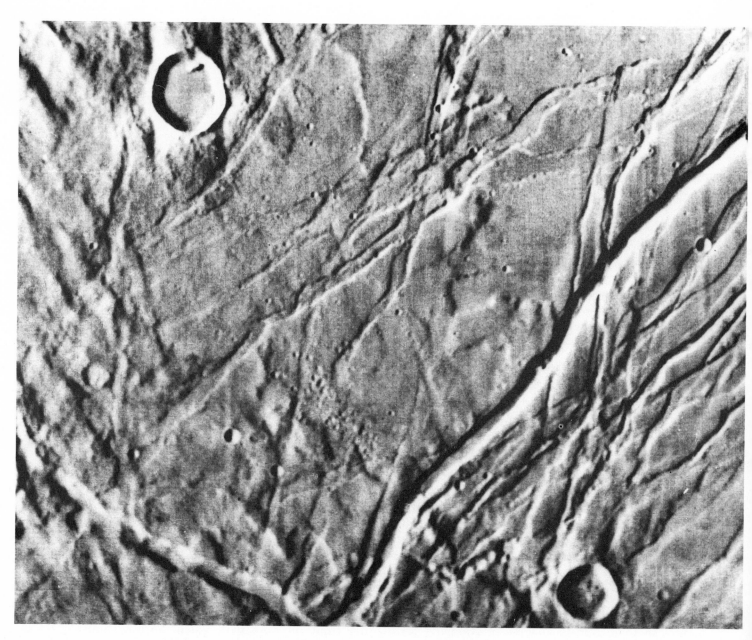

Fractured and faulted terrain about 2000 kilometers northeast of the Tharsis volcanic dome at 82°, +31°. (1434–180111)

Geologic map of Mars indicating Tharsis (*t*) and Elysium (*e*) volcanic domed regions and associated radial fractures. Small letters show various geologic provinces, explained in chapter 11.

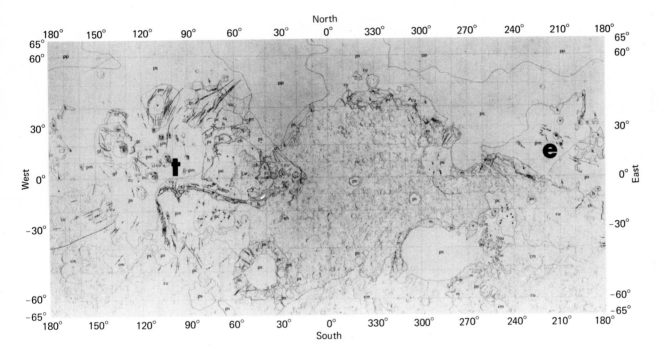

The "chaotic terrain," or jumbled craggy lowlands discovered by Mariners 6 and 7, lie at the east end of Aurorae Sinus, on a line with Coprates. As the 1971 dust storm cleared, Coprates became apparent not in its usual guise of a dark streak, but as a straight, bright, cloudlike band. As the atmosphere cleared, it became evident that this was a dust cloud lying in a deep valley. Finally the dust settled out of even this lowest part of the atmosphere, and the Vallis Marineris was revealed. The canyon can be traced in nearly linear band for 4000 kilometers from its latticelike, fractured western end to the very low, chaotic terrain at its east end, a distance of more than one-sixth of the planetary circumference. Numerous branching tributary canyons enter it. At its widest points it approaches 200 kilometers in width and its depth reaches as much as 6 kilometers (nearly 20 000 feet) below its rim, according to ultraviolet-spectroscopy-measured altitudes. For comparison, the Grand Canyon is only about 150 kilometers long, 6 to 28 kilometers in width, and about 2 kilometers (less than 7000 feet) in

(Continued on page 91)

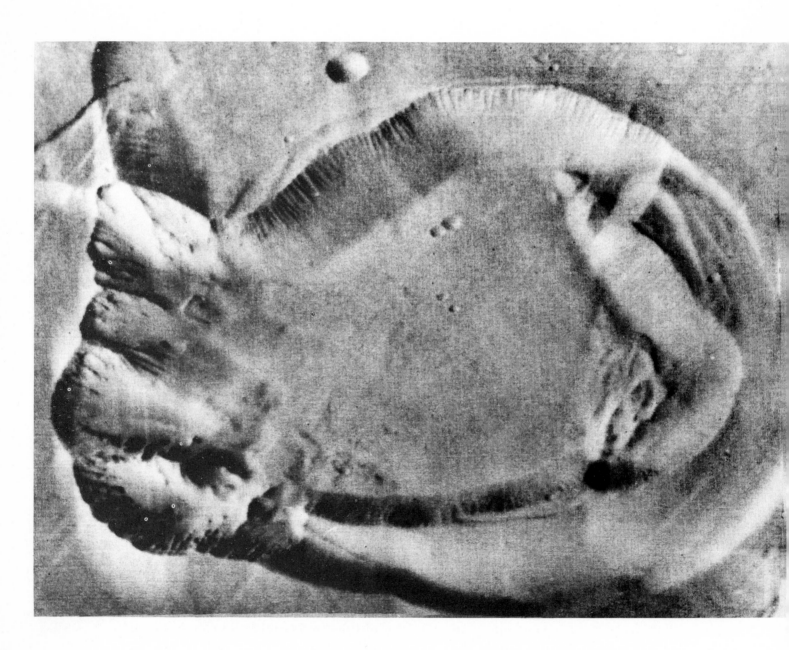

Caldera of a volcano located east of Ascraeus Mons at 91°, +14°. Rim displays upper fluted cliffs and lower talus slopes, as well as evidence of multiple collapse. The caldera diameter is approximately 60 kilometers. (1434–174452)

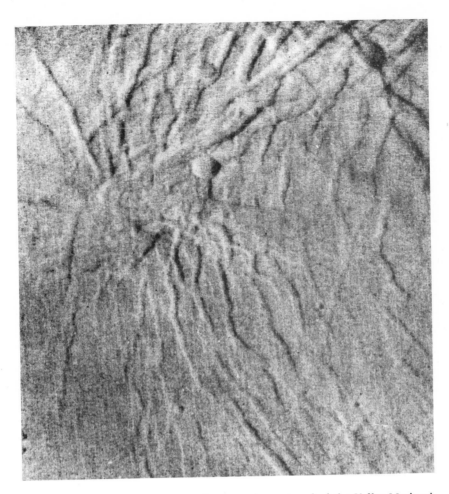

The "elephant skin" fracture complex near the west end of the Valles Marineris canyon complex, near 109°, —17°.

mantle and crust of Mars. They believe that horizontal motions in the Martian crust are not as great as in Earth's crust because Mars does not display the crumpled and folded mountain belts, such as the Rockies, Andes, and Himalayas, that mark terrestrial sites where crustal plates collide. On the other hand, the Martian patterns suggest a sort of incipient plate tectonics in which ascending hot currents in the Martian mantle disrupt the crust and cause volcanism, but perhaps do not last long enough to cause full-fledged horizontal drifting of crustal blocks.

The beauty of the Martian evidence is that Mars has no oceans to mask the deepest rifts in its crust. Thus Mars presents a plain display of the results of forces that terrestrial geologists have speculated about and glimpsed with great difficulty by means of complex deep-sea experiments. One of the main results of the Mariner 9 mission—unexpectedly—is thus likely to be a tying together of many loose ends left in terrestrial geology by the revolution of the last decade, when, in the face of new evidence, the view of continents as fixed, near-permanent rock units gave way to a view of changing, colliding crustal blocks driven by forces deep in Earth's mantle.

CHAPTER VIII

Channels and the Evidence for Ancient Rivers

. . . there must be rivers on Mars. . . . The mere existence of continents and oceans on Mars proves the action of forces of upheaval and of depression. There must be volcanic eruptions and earthquakes, modeling and remodeling the crust of Mars. Thus there must be mountains and hills, valleys and ravines, watersheds and watercourses.

—R. A. Proctor, 1871

. . . spectrographic results and the . . . indications derived from the polar caps . . . agree in pointing to a much higher degree of dryness in the bright equatorial regions of Mars than in the most arid terrestrial deserts.

This extreme desiccation is in excellent agreement with the whole body of observations. . . .

—G. de Vaucouleurs, 1954

In terms of fitting Mariner 9's new information to pre-Mariner 9 information, the most astonishing discovery was that of widespread channels that bear every conceivable resemblance to dry riverbeds. They are not the linear "canals" that were once shown on maps nor do they coincide with them except in a few instances; rather, they are prominent, meander sinuously, and include short branching tributary systems. The idea that these really are riverbeds seems at first glance to fly in the face of all information about the current state of Martian climatology. As for present-day conditions, de Vaucouleurs was right in the introductory quotation. For example, the total amount of water vapor in the Martian atmosphere is so small that if all the water on a typical day precipitated in the form of rain, it would make a

layer only 0.002 to 0.005 centimeter deep according to Earth-based and Mariner 9 infrared interferometer spectrometer data. Furthermore, if water did accumulate by some means, the pressure of the air is so low and the temperature so cold that in most regions of Mars it would spontaneously boil away or freeze. This behavior would occur in all regions having elevation higher than the Martian reference level, which has an atmospheric pressure of 6.1 millibars.

This particular pressure, whether on Mars or elsewhere, is the so-called triple-point pressure; it is the minimum pressure at which liquid water can exist in equilibrium with its gaseous vapor. Thus at lower pressures it boils or freezes, depending on the temperature; at higher pressures it can exist as a liquid in equilibrium, but it evaporates if the atmosphere is dry enough. At exactly 6.105 millibars and 273.01° Kelvin (32° Fahrenheit), the three phases of water—gas, liquid, and solid—can all exist together in equilibrium; hence the name "triple point."

Locations on Mars at elevations below the reference level at 6.1 millibars—i.e., locations with greater atmospheric pressure—could have liquid water that would not spontaneously boil. Nonetheless, temperatures above 273° Kelvin would be required for liquid water, and such temperatures exist only on the warmest afternoons in summer near the equator. If liquid water does occur, evaporation could be rapid, depending on the local temperature and water vapor pressure in the atmosphere. According to calculations by physical chemist C. B. Farmer, the evaporation rate under summer afternoon

Enlarged mosaic of Vallis Maadim showing tributary system at south end. (4167–18, 4167–24)

Channel in Xanthe-Chryse area near 45°, −5° named Vallis Shalbatana. Downhill slope is north (*top*) toward low region of Mare Acidaleum. Note finer sinuous channels, left. The length of the channel is about 1200 kilometers. (Jet Propulsion Laboratory mosaic, 211–4646)

Enlarged mosaic of Vallis Nirgal in Mare Erythraeum showing details of the tributary system and central meandering portion.

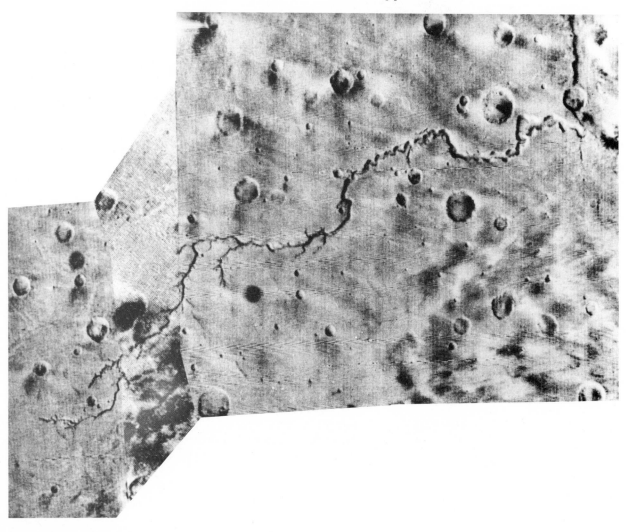

Telephoto view of braided channels associated with Vallis Mangala, in the Amazonis region near 150°, −6°. Such deposits are normally attributed to sediments dropped during meandering stream flow. North is at top; each frame measures about 30 by 40 kilometers. (4258–35; 4258–39)

Terrestrial example of braided deposits in the Sagavanir-tok River, Alaska. Note truncated downstream ends of bars (flow toward top). Compare with Martian example at left. The width is 2 kilometers. (U.S. Navy photograph BAR 2830955, U.S. Geological Survey)

Martian temperatures would be about 2 centimeters per hour. A foot-deep rivulet might evaporate between dawn and dusk even in those parts of Mars where liquid water is favored.

So the proposition of rivers on Mars was greeted with skepticism on two counts: it seems to require a miracle to get large volumes of water on the surface of Mars and it seems to require another miracle to keep the water there long enough to erode a river channel.

Faced with this dilemma, the initial reaction of Mariner 9 scientists was to consider the alternatives. Could lava flows cut the channels? The braided deposits in their floors suggested that the fluid carried sediments unlike lavas, and the channels were not limited to highly volcanic terrains. Could the channels be cut by some liquid other than water? No suggestions were forthcoming on what such an abundant liquid could be; liquid carbon dioxide, for example, would require five times the atmospheric pressure that exists at Earth's surface. Could they be cut by some sort of exotic fluidized suspension of dust particles in the wind? In terrestrial volcanic eruptions of a certain type, the hot volcanic gases can trap fine ash particles creating a fluidlike mass that flows down mountainsides and spreads across plains. Such a mass—known as a *nuee ardente*—was responsible for destroying the city of St. Pierre, Martinique, with the loss of 30 000 lives in 1902. Such systems, however, are not known to erode winding riverlike systems with tributaries. In view of the low atmospheric pressures on Mars and the lack of good terrestrial analogs, the hypothesis of windcut "river channels" seemed unsupportable.

The more careful the scrutiny of the channels, the stronger the conviction became that they were similar to dry arroyos cut by sediment-carrying waters in terrestrial arid regions. For example, the major channel crossing the Amazonis area, west of Tharsis, contains a complex of braided channels and bars of the type that develop when sediments build deposits in meandering rivers and subsequent meanders of the flowing channel then cut across the already formed bars. Named Vallis, this channel as a whole is about 350 kilometers in length and consists of a complex of individual channels. Geomorphologists studying the orientation of the streamlined and truncated bars in the channel suggest that the flow direction was from south to north. A similar situation applies in the channel complex of the Chryse region, east of Tharsis. The flow direction appears to run about 1200 kilometers from the chaotic terrain at the east end of the Vallis Marineris toward the broad featureless plains near Mare Acidalium. This is consistent with the altimetry data in the area, which show that the latter regions are lower than the former, although such evidence is not conclusive because crustal deformation might have altered the topography since the channels formed. The geomorphological analysis of the channels indicates that they were cut by a high-density, low-viscosity, sediment-carrying true liquid confined to the channel. Water appears to be the only acceptable possibility.

With flowing water as the only viable hypothesis to account for the channels, and with no evident contemporary source of surface water, analysts turned to consideration of conditions in the past history of Mars. In addition to the mere existence of the channels, there are several other indications that the past climatology of Mars might have been more conducive to river formation than the present climatology. First, subtleties of impact crater distribution and morphology suggest greater rates of erosion and deposition in the past than at present. The few examples of craters superimposed on channels indicate that they formed in the past but not in the extremely distant past. Also, the low temperatures prevailing on Mars now mean that large amounts of water would, if they existed, be mostly frozen somewhere on the planet. "Somewhere" could mean in the permanent polar caps, in mixed layers of dust and ice deposited in the polar regions (which are observed to contain layered terrains—see later chapters), buried widespread ice deposits resembling permafrost deposits in terrestrial tundra, or other unknown forms of ice deposits. In support of this, spectrophotometric data from Earth-based observers such as T. McCord, A. Binder, J. Houck, and others have led to suggestions of water frosts mixed with Martian surface soils, perhaps to about 1 percent by weight. Also, theoretical work such as that of F. Fanale suggests abundant water should be available on Mars.

The permafrost hypothesis is supported by the existence of the Martian chaotic terrain, which

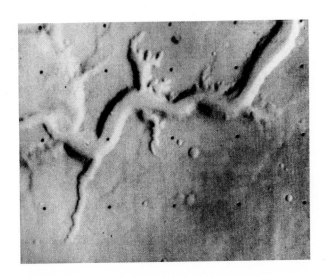

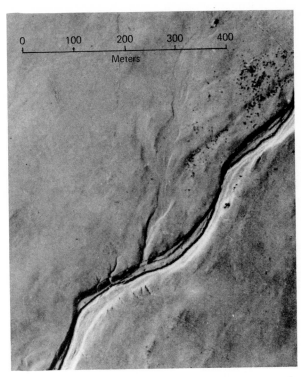

Tributaries to a channel in Moab, near 339°, +31°. The width of the channel is about 5 kilometers. (1417–221824)

Terrestrial example of a channel cut in an extremely dry region in the coastal desert of Peru. Typical of arroyos in arid regions is the stubby tributary system and multiple channel pattern on the arroyo floor. (U.S. Geological Survey)

Artist's conception of the appearance of a Martian channel showing braided deposits. (Ludek Pesek, © 1973, National Geographic Society)

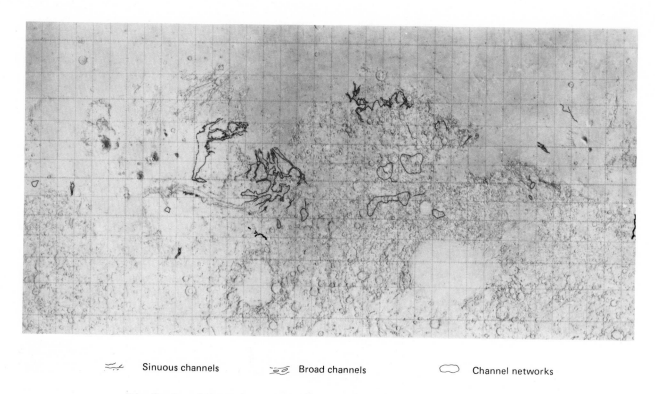

| ~⊰ | Sinuous channels | ⇌⊸ | Broad channels | ◯ | Channel networks |

Distribution of channels on Mars showing classification into three general types.

resembles collapsed, rugged terrain produced when deposits of subsurface ice melt by some source of heat, such as local volcanic or geothermal activity, or seasonal or secular climatic warming. Such collapsed areas appear on a much smaller scale in arctic regions of Earth and are known as thermokarst topography—from the term "karst," referring to a collapsed pit. This explanation of chaotic terrain, which was first suggested by geologists R. Sharp, L. Soderblom, B. Murray, and J. Cutts in their analysis of Mariner 6 and 7 photographs, is further strongly supported by the fact that the Martian "river

channels" frequently appear to emanate from the regions of chaotic terrain. One is led to speculate that under some warming condition in the past, underground permafrost melted, causing collapse of surface layers and release of a flood of water that rushed over the surface, cutting channels through loose, windblown deposits.

Mariner 9 geologists and geomorphologists who have studied the structures at the edges and "sources" of the channels have pointed to fractured and slumped terrain that suggests not only stream cutting and collapse from below but an additional process known as ground-water sap-

Gullied slopes on a volcano in Alba, near 116°, +45°. The dendritic pattern is similar to erosion patterns on alluvial slopes in arid terrestrial regions. The frame width is about 60 kilometers. (4182–96)

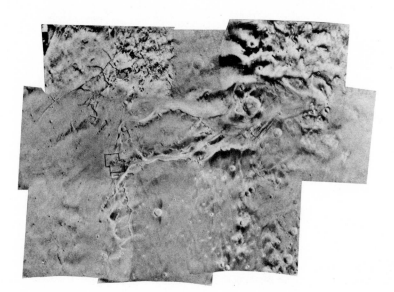

Channel complex in Lunae Palus, near 65°, +22°. Flow direction is east (*right*) toward the Mare Acidalium area. Note isolated fractures and chaotic terrain in northwest. Box marks location of additional fractured terrain shown in telephoto view below. (Jet Propulsion Laboratory mosaic 211–4653)

Dendritic canyon and fracture system near west end of Lunae Palus channel, near 73°, +22°. The pattern suggests extension of the canyon along fractures widened by removal of material. Note ejecta blanket of crater, upper right, which has withstood erosion. The frame width is about 50 kilometers. (4297–8, 4297–12)

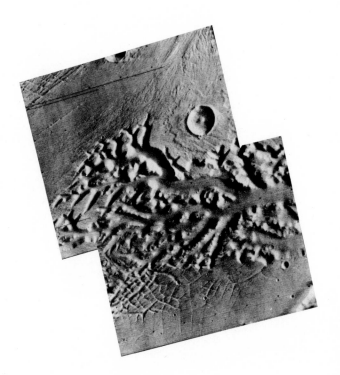

ping. This occurs when ground water seeps directly toward and out of the exposed valley walls, causing slumping of the ground. Thus the channel expands by having its walls cut back, instead of only downward. A variant of this process, perhaps more applicable to contemporary Mars, is ground *ice* sapping. In this process, a permafrost layer of underground ice, exposed by any mechanism such as river channeling or faulting, begins to sublime or melt. This releases entrained gravel and causes a void; the associated cliff face collapses, exposing new ice. If the rubble is continually removed by wind or water, the process continues and the cliff or channel wall continues to retreat. It has been suggested that large areas of Mars have been denuded and reduced to low elevation by this process, which may have widened channels or chaotic terrain since the rivers last contained liquid water. An example of a region where this may have occurred is the west-facing cliff face bordering the channel at the east edge of the Tharsis region.

The shape of several other Martian channels supports the idea that they are enlarged by ground water or ice sapping. For example, several of the "small" tributary canyons to the great Vallis Marineris are similar in size and appearance to the Grand Canyon of the Colorado River. Each has stubby side canyons ending at steep headwalls. The Grand Canyon is known to involve ground-water sapping by artesian springs that undermine the headwalls; a similar process may cause the similar forms on Mars. A long narrow channel of quite different form occurs on Mars in the Rasena region. In its lower reaches it resembles the sinuous rilles of the Moon, believed to be the channels of lava flows that have formed not so much by excavation as by processes involving the solidification of lava at the walls of the flow. In its upper reaches, the Rasena channel has tributaries like those of other Martian channels and distinctly unlike any lava flow features. The tributary system again suggests water flow (unlike volcanic flows that generally have a discrete source), but the analogy to molten lava/solid rock interfaces again suggests liquid water running through ice layers, with associated ground ice sapping.

Mariner 9 geologists have noted that many Martian channel systems seem immature and discordant with their local terrain, suggesting sporadic catastrophic flooding rather than gradual, smooth evolution. On Earth, such channels may arise in arid regions where infrequent major floods accompany local downpours. Another example is the most violent known flood, produced during the prehistoric catastrophic discharge of Lake Missoula, whose ice dam broke, releasing a torrent 70 times the average discharge rate of the Amazon River. This torrent produced the Mars-like erosional landform known as the Channel Scablands in the State of Washington.

Clearly we have passed from the realm of direct photographic discovery to a realm of difficult interpretation by analogy and inference. Mariner 9 analysts believe they have located important pieces of the channel puzzle—flowing water, past warmer climates and greater atmospheric pressure, ground ice or permafrost, removal of debris by water or wind, and sporadic flow—but the pieces have not yet fallen into place to produce a satisfying picture.

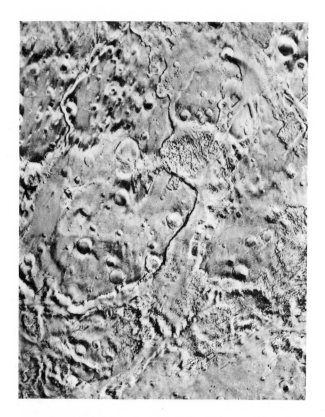

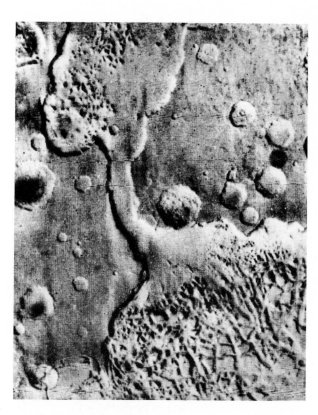

Association of Vallis Simud channels and chaotic terrain, near Chryse, centered near 35°, —4°. The frame height is about 1250 kilometers. The lower part of the frame includes the east end of the Valles Marineris complex. (Jet Propulsion Laboratory globe)

Detail of channel near Chryse near 32°, —3°, showing association with chaotic terrain. The frame height is about 480 kilometers. (7350–165312)

The clues go far beyond the striking suggestion that Mars was more Earth-like in the past. They raise the questions of the cause of the changes of climate, of whether there was one or more changes, and of whether the changes were long-term slow changes or sudden catastrophic changes. These questions have stimulated much theorizing about Mars. For example, studies of the small uneroded craters, in contrast to the large eroded craters, suggests a geologically sudden transition from past erosive conditions to present less erosive conditions on Mars. More exciting is the fact that these questions may reflect on ancient terrestrial conditions.

An approach to the problem lies in the origin and atmospheric behavior of the water on Mars and Earth. How did the atmospheres and water content of Earth and Mars originate? It is widely believed that a massive primitive atmosphere of gases such as hydrogen, methane, and ammonia must have been left after planet formation. This atmosphere is believed to have dwindled over a

number, largely because of the lack of information concerning the atmosphere and surface of Mars and the consequent tendency to interpret all observations in terms of Earth analogies. It was not until 50 years later that astrophysical studies were undertaken to discern the true nature of the polar caps, first by Kuiper in 1948 and later by Dollfus in 1950. Both experiments were based on the reflective properties of the cap material, and in each case the experimenters concluded the material was water ice. Whereas Mariner 4 did not view the polar cap in 1965, the occultation data showed the atmosphere to be essentially carbon dioxide at a few millibars pressure, and this led to strong new arguments by Murray, Leighton, and Leovy as well as others that the caps were primarily carbon dioxide. Mariner 7 made the first closeup observations of the south polar cap in 1969, and whereas the temperatures measured by both the infrared instruments were consistent with a frozen carbon dioxide cap, the data were insufficient to settle the question. Mariner 7 seemed to dim the prospects for a polar "melt band"; no dark area of any kind was observed around the receding cap.

Mariner 9 photographed the south polar region of Mars from November 1971 until March 1972. The time at which the spacecraft arrived corresponded to early summer in the southern hemisphere of Mars, and the polar cap was in the late stages of its retreat. In contrast to pictures taken by Mariner 7, the first Mariner 9 pictures showed the cap edge to be sharply defined, with very few isolated frost patches outside the cap or "windows" in the cap. This implied that the cap's boundaries were determined by underlying terrain that was relatively smooth and free from topographical irregularities. These boundaries continued to retreat for about 3 weeks after Mariner 9's arrival, but changed very little during the remainder of the mission.

Earth-based observations had never unambiguously established the presence of a residual cap in the southern hemisphere of Mars, and the observation of a stable cap remnant during the 1972 opposition was a significant result of the Mariner 9 mission. Calculations made by Mariner 9 scientists studying the cap suggested the evaporation rate of solid carbon dioxide might be too high during the Martian southern summer to permit a residual cap of this material to survive. On the other hand, the vapor pressure of water ice at the polar temperatures would be quite low, and the slow evaporation rate of a cap composed of water ice would permit it to survive indefinitely. Thus the Mariner 9 experimenters proposed that the primary cap, which comes and goes with the seasons, is mostly carbon dioxide, but that the residual cap left each year is possibly water ice. If this view is correct, it goes a long way toward answering the question raised in the preceding chapter as to the location of the "missing" water on Mars: it may be locked in residual ice caps that do not melt now, but may have melted under warmer conditions in the geologic past. Some experimenters suggested the water ice caps may have originally formed because of a large atmospheric influx of water vapor during some past epochal event such as the formation of the large volcanoes mentioned in the previous chapter as possible sources for water vapor. The persistence of the caps through the Martian spring and summer, during the time when entrained water is being released by the subliming carbon dioxide,

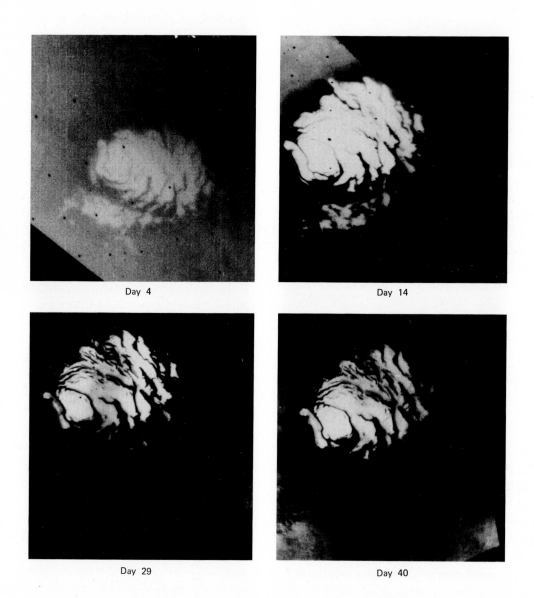

Four views of the shrinking south polar cap showing the development of a residual cap during 37 days of Mariner 9 photography. The first view shows the cap shrouded in dust from the 1971 dust storm. By day 14 this dust has cleared, but the cap's outline, about 300 by 350 kilometers, changes little thereafter. (P12803)

may also imply they are slowly growing through a process of accretion of this water vapor from the atmosphere. This growth process may in turn be modified or reversed by long-term cyclic changes in conditions on Mars associated with precession of both its own spin axis and its perihelion, or point of closest approach to the Sun, during the planet's orbit. Although these ideas are still unproven, they indicate that we are probably close to a final answer to the long-debated question of the composition of the Martian polar caps. Future research will be directed in earnest toward the Martian polar caps, which have emerged as a result of the Mariner 9 mission as key features in the Martian environment.

In 1969, during the Mariner 7 photography, the south polar cap was in a very extended early spring stage. The arrival time and orbital parameters selected for Mariner 9 were nearly ideal for high-resolution frostfree coverage of the region that had been frost covered. Special interest attached to this region because Mariner 7 had shown hints of an unusual type of sparsely cratered terrain there. Mariner 9 photographs more than justified this interest. The early Mariner 9 pictures revealed a vast area of terrain in the region of and encompassing the pole with a relatively smooth, uncratered surface, ending in a graceful, sinuous staircase of slopes descending to the apparently more ancient terrain below. The layers were stacked like saucers of various sizes, and their edges defined curving contours around the residual cap. The descriptive term "layered" was adopted for this terrain, and subsequent mapping proved it to exist at both the

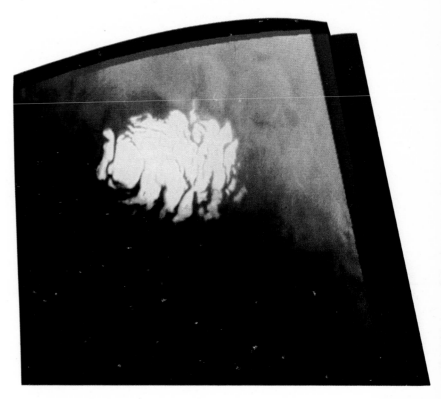

The south polar cap of Mars in color, in a reconstructed view using photography with different color filters. The terminator, or sunset line, slants across the bottom of the picture. (Jet Propulsion Laboratory Image Processing Laboratory 211–4641)

north and south poles, but to be unique to the polar regions.

The presence of the layered terrain on Mars was an intriguing discovery, perhaps comparable in significance to the subsequent discoveries of riverlike channels and the great crustal disturbances of the volcanic province. What caused the layered structure? What were the layers composed of? How was the material transported and deposited? Could the Martian dust storms be involved? Considering these questions, some members of the Mariner 9 television team drew the initial conclusion that formation of the laminated terrain involved either water or carbon dioxide, or both, because the phenomenon was

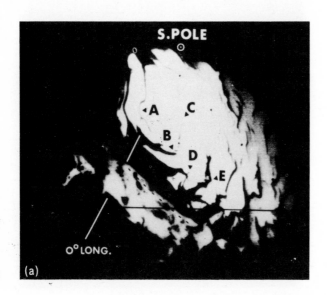
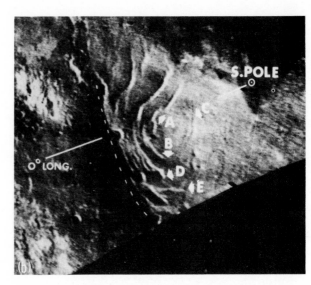

Comparison of features in residual southern cap (*a*) with the same features in the snow-covered cap photographed by Mariner 7 in 1969 (*b*). Although (*b*) shows a region entirely snow covered, it has been printed with darker tone to show features within the cap itself. The arcuate features, labeled *A* to *E*, may be ridges related to stratified deposits near the pole.

restricted to the polar region where volatiles were regularly condensed and evaporated. They suggested that fine dust and volcanic ash, circulated by the frequent dust storms, could easily be entrained by volatiles condensing there and accumulated into stratified deposits; subsequent evaporation of the volatiles would then leave a deposit much like sedimentary rock on Earth. Alternatively, the water ice or carbon dioxide ice might still be present as a part of the layers. Partial erosion due to ice evaporation might then explain the observed rounded edges. Finally, one of the cyclic changes previously mentioned in connection with Mars' orbit oc-

curs with a period of 95 000 years, and this periodic modification of the Martian seasons was postulated as being responsible for the layered nature of the deposits and their resultant thickness.

Other Mariner investigators disagreed with the postulate that the 95 000-year cycle was responsible for layer formation, arguing that the observed thicknesses of the individual layers represented amounts of material far in excess of that which could be transported and deposited in the polar regions in such a geologically short period. An additional periodicity occurs in Mars' orbit with a 2-million-year cycle, and these

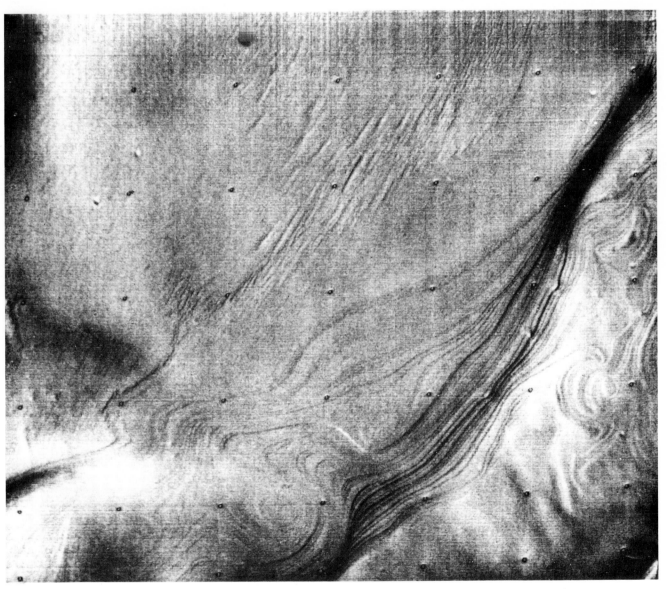

Laminated terrain in the south polar region near 229°, −75°. Laminations descend from smooth, striated uplands (*center*) to low, sinuous features (*right*). (The light comes from the left.) The thinnest laminations are believed to be about 30 meters thick. Depth of area in this photograph is about 50 kilometers. Striations in center of frame are interpreted as wind erosion features from strong prevailing winds. (4213–21)

Raised and pitted layer near 325°, −66°. Width of smooth plateau is about 70 kilometers. Striations on its surface are attributed to erosion by strong prevailing winds. (The light comes from the left.) (P–12752)

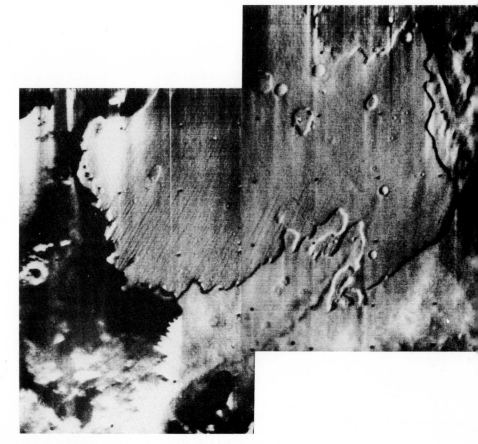

Oval, laminated tableland near the south pole, 84°, −82°. The stratified area appears to overlie older, pitted terrain that emerges at the bottom. Sunlight comes from 10° above the horizon at the left. The frame dimension is about 47 by 60 kilometers. (P–12925)

Possible terrestrial analog of Martian laminated terrain. Freezing conditions in Kelso dunes, southern California, led to wind etching of stratified layers within the dunes. Width between main dark bands is about 2 meters. (Robert P. Sharp)

investigators considered this period to be more compatible with the time necessary to form the observed layers. They proposed that the variation in insolation at perihelion associated with the 2-million-year cycle modulates the occurrence of global-scale dust storms, and that this modulation is responsible for layer formation.

An entirely different hypothesis concerning layer formation was proposed by one Mariner scientist, based on the triple point of carbon dioxide. He proposed that a process much like glacier formation on Earth could occur in the carbon dioxide deposits at the Martian poles once the deposits became heavy enough. Under the proper conditions, liquid carbon dioxide could be formed at the bottom, flow out, and subsequently refreeze.

These ideas, whereas they might account for the formation of layers, left a number of other mysteries unanswered. For example, the edges of the layered deposits tended to define contour-like arcs not only with different sizes but with apparently different centers. Why did the arcs of different radii seem to have different centers? One early published analysis by Mariner 9 investigators suggested that Mars undergoes polar wandering—a phenomenon known on Earth—by which the polar position, and hence the point of symmetry for layered deposits, changes. This might cause each cyclic layer to be deposited with a different center.

Whereas the ultimate origin of the polar layered terrain is less than certain, the processes modifying these units have been clarified by studies of television photographs and theoretical analysis of Martian winds near the poles. The surfaces of these units are frequently scoured with fine parallel striations a few hundred meters in width and many kilometers long. The units are also pitted with irregular depressions, or "etch pits," many kilometers in diameter. Study of the striations revealed that they were generally oriented nearly radially to the pole, but with a spiral pattern centered at the pole. These patterns are similar to theoretically predicted patterns for Martian polar winds, and it is believed that they represent wind erosion patterns. Similarly, the irregular pits are interpreted by many observers as deflation basins, excavated when loose material at some point in one of the layered units is blown out by the wind. Similar deflation basins appear in terrestrial deserts.

What were the relations between these various polar terrain units? Although absolute ages of the distinctive types are not certain, the absence of craters on the surface of the layered terrain indicates it is quite young compared to other Martian structures. Counts of craters suggest the polar surfaces are as young as or younger than the large volcanoes. In several photographs it is apparent that the escarpments forming borders

of layers were only partially obscuring the features of the underlying terrain. The underlying terrain could additionally be separated into two types, the first being characterized as "etch pitted" and the second as the cratered terrain relatively common to Mars. While the layered terrain obviously overlaid both the cratered and etch-pitted terrain, there were similar indications that the etch-pitted areas overlaid the cratered terrain. Thus the relative ages of the observed terrain ap-

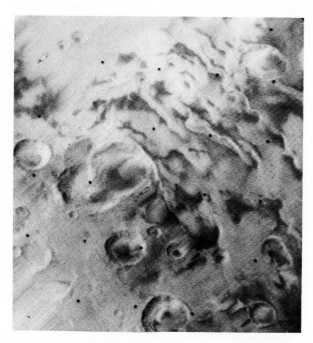

Channellike escarpments in the south polar area near 154°, —74°. Picture width is about 420 kilometers; south pole is out of the frame to the left. (1697–170347)

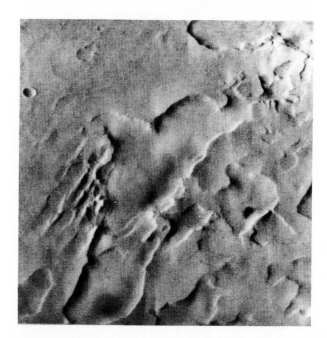

Irregular pits in south polar terrain near 93°, —77°. These may be old craters and other irregular features being etched or deflated by wind removal of deposits. Fresh crater at upper left is about 4 kilometers in diameter. (1589–134624)

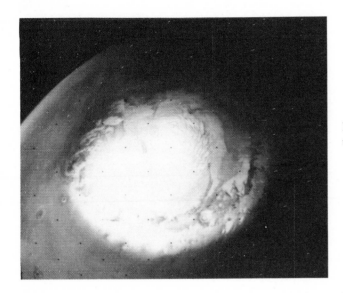

North polar cap showing craters and other interior detail during retreat. (4296–102)

North polar cap showing formation of residual permanent cap with spiral lanes and surrounding dark annulus, possibly related to the "melt band" long reported by Earth-based observers. (4297–46)

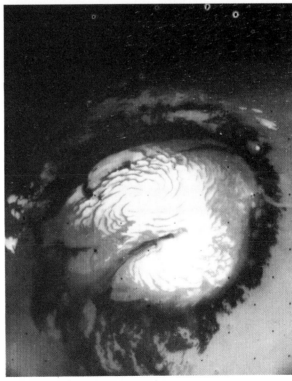

June, the north cap had already begun its recession. Thus Mariner 9 began monitoring the cap when it was about 85 percent of its original size and continued to monitor it until it had receded to a perennial cap similar to that found in the south. The rate at which the cap receded conformed closely to that predicted from Earth-based observations and the Leighton-Murray calculations based on carbon dioxide sublimation. The abrupt halt in this retreat and the relative stability of the remaining portion of the cap again suggested that this permanent residue might be water ice. Temperatures measured by the infrared radiometer tend to support this hypothesis. In some of the high-altitude pictures taken during the early stages of recession, the outline of the cap appeared to be polygonal; this shape seemed to be maintained during the cap's retreat, with all sides receding at roughly the same rate. It was suggested that the outline might be controlled by regional topography, which had been modified by the loading of the polar region with thick deposits. On a smaller scale, it was apparent that local topography controlled the persistence or loss of frost at the edge of the retreating cap.

The terrain features in the north polar region were essentially identical to those observed in the south. The relatively smooth, layered plains with their graceful escarpments, overlaying both etch-pitted and cratered terrain, were character-istic of both polar regions. Perhaps the major difference between the two regions, inferred from occultation measurements and spectrom-eter data, lay in the relative abundances of the polar deposits and their possible influence on the observed shape of Mars.

A final feature of the north polar cap brings us back to a problem raised at the beginning of this chapter: the existence or nonexistence of a dark polar "melt band" supposedly surrounding the cap as it begins to shrink. Late in the Mariner 9 mission, afer north polar haze cleared and the north cap began to shrink, Mariner 9 sent back several excellent photographs of the north cap and its surroundings, and these photographs showed a terrain of low albedo surrounding the cap. This terrain, when viewed from the Earth, could easily have been interpreted by early observers as a "melt band" following the receding cap. However, it appears to be a fixed surface feature, not a band of temporarily moist soil.

As we have pursued the Martian volatiles, particularly water, to their possible reservoir in the Martian polar caps, it has become clear that we must consider the Martian atmosphere and its important roles as transport medium for volatiles, modifier of the surface material, and repository for clouds and hazes. This topic will be taken up in the next chapter.

CHAPTER X

The Atmosphere

*I believe it will be possible in the future to fore-
tell, with something approaching the certainty of
our esteemed weather bureaus' prognostications, not
indeed what the weather will be on Mars—for, as we
have seen, it is more than doubtful whether Mars
has what we call a weather to prognosticate—but the
aspect of the planet at any given time.*
—PERCIVAL LOWELL, 1895

When Herschel and the other scientists of
the early 1800's were providing Mars with a
population through hypothesis, they did not fail
to endow the planet with an atmosphere much
like that of Earth. This was an assumed necessity, because life as we know it is markedly
dependent in many ways on the specific constituents of our atmosphere, as well as the relative abundances. Liquid water is a fundamental
necessity to the life process on Earth, and while
the presence of water vapor in the atmosphere
does not necessarily signify the existence of
liquid water on the surface, the absence of
water vapor is a positive indication that no
liquid water is present. With the exception of
some lower life forms called anaerobes, free
molecular oxygen is also required to sustain
Earth's living organisms. Thus it was no coincidence that the first crude attempt by Janssen
and Huggins at spectroscopic analysis of the
Martian atmosphere was performed primarily
to determine the presence or absence of molecular oxygen and water vapor.

A more indirect but equally necessary atmospheric function for sustaining terrestrial life is
the screening out of the Sun's lethal ultraviolet
radiation. In the case of Earth, this function is
performed by the ozone layer in the strato-
sphere: the ozone completely absorbs all of the
short-wavelength radiation and dissipates it in
a dissociation-recombination process that ultimately converts the ultraviolet light into other
harmless forms of energy. In the absence of an
ozone layer or its equivalent for shielding the
surface, life forms on other planets would have
to have evolved within themselves some protection mechanism, or be perennially restricted to
an existence that avoided direct contact with
sunlight.

In addition to deriving protection and sus-
tenance from the atmosphere, life forms may
also contribute to its content. For example, the
ammonia, methane, and other small hydrocar-
bon molecules present as trace constituents in
Earth's atmosphere are all there as a result of
present or past life processes. Thus, a great
deal of excitement was generated among those
present at a press conference shortly after
Mariner 7 had flown by Mars when it was
announced that preliminary analysis of the data
from the infrared spectrometer experiment revealed two small spectral features attributable
to methane and ammonia. However, subsequent
analysis did not support the initial conclusions:
the spectra containing the two features had
been recorded in the vicinity of the south polar
cap and were ultimately identified as two seldom-
seen absorption bands of solid carbon dioxide.

Whereas the biological implications that can
be inferred from atmospheric studies have a
strong popular appeal, they represent only a

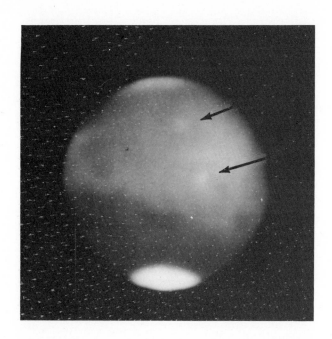

Photographs from Earth in blue light show Martian atmospheric features such as clouds and hazes. This example shows two bright clouds near the positions of the volcanoes Olympus Mons (top) and Arsia Mons (bottom). (August 12, 1971; University of Arizona Lunar and Planetary Laboratory)

small fraction of the total information such studies provide with regard to the planet itself. The atmosphere, after all, provides the surface environment and affects surface processes. An accurate knowledge of the present state of a planet's atmosphere, including the types of species present and their abundances, atmospheric temperature profiles, the photochemical processes occurring, and the formation and movement of clouds and dust storms, is of inestimable value to scientists who are attempting to

deduce the past and future history of the planet and explain any periodic or sporadic changes occurring on the surface. For example, the water vapor content in the Martian atmosphere was known from pre-Mariner 9 measurements to be quite low, and this seems unlike the atmosphere that would accompany a planet with features appearing to be riverbeds. If these features imply the presence of liquid water in the past, where is it now? If it has been photochemically dissociated to hydrogen and oxygen, what has been the fate of these species? Hydrogen, because of its low atomic weight, would ultimately escape from the planet's gravitational field, and its escape rate was actually measured by Mariner 9.

By monitoring the strong emission line at 1216 nanometers, the ultraviolet spectroscopy experimenters were able to measure the atomic hydrogen concentration in the upper atmosphere of Mars and calculate the rate at which it was escaping from the planet. The value found for the escape rate was 2×10^8 atoms per second per square centimeter through an imaginary surface at the top of the atmosphere. If the only source for hydrogen atoms on Mars is water, this represents a loss of water from Mars of about 1 million gallons per day. If Mars has lost water at this rate since its formation, the total water that has escaped would be sufficient to cover the entire surface of the planet to a depth of 5 meters! Projecting this escape rate into the future, an amount equivalent to the total water vapor now present in the atmosphere will be lost in less than 100 000 years.

Does this imply we have begun our closeup observations of Mars only to learn that the planet

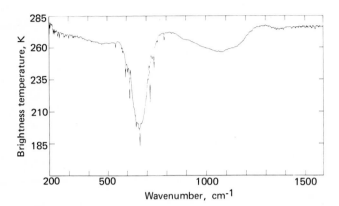

Martian spectrum obtained by Mariner 9 infrared spectrometer on December 29, 1971, during final clearing of the dust storm. Dips are caused by absorptions due to dust particles. Shape of absorption dips can be related to particle size, indicating airborne dust particles about 2 to 20 micrometers in diameter. Other spectra revealed data on atmospheric pressure and composition.

is in the final stages of dehydration as suggested by Lowell? Probably not. There is unquestionably water ice stored in the polar caps and in the form of permafrost, and the volcanoes may provide an additional source of water vapor to the atmosphere. Also, the assumption that water vapor is the sole source of atomic hydrogen in the Martian atmosphere is based on the lack of evidence to the contrary, rather than positive evidence that such is the case. Two alternate but unlikely sources of hydrogen atoms have been suggested: the thermalization of solar-wind protons (hydrogen ions) in the upper atmosphere or the presence on the planet of a continuous source of molecular hydrogen, a molecule neither spectrometer would have been able to detect. One factor arguing mildly against

the water vapor hypothesis for the source of escaping hydrogen—again assuming the hydrogen atom escape rate has been constant throughout the history of Mars—is the amount of oxygen that would have been produced in the photolytic process. The present concentration of molecular oxygen in the atmosphere is only a few millionths of the amount that would have been generated. However, it is possible that a great deal of this oxygen could have been used up in surface oxidation; astrophysicist Michael McElroy has also suggested a possible mechanism for the escape of atomic oxygen through recombination reactions of the major ions in Mars' ionosphere.

The ionospheric region of an atmosphere is characterized by the presence of charged species, or ions, that are produced as a result of interactions between the neutral atmospheric species and high-energy photons and electrons from the Sun. The base of the region is defined by the depth to which these photons and electrons can penetrate; and the top, called the exosphere, is considered to be that region above which collisions between particles no longer occur because of the extremely low densities. Thus, particles passing outward through the ionosphere with sufficient velocity to overcome the gravitational forces of the planet will probably escape the planet permanently. The highly energetic processes continuously occurring in the ionosphere cause temperatures higher than those in any other region of the atmosphere; at the exosphere, temperatures begin to fall off rapidly. This ionospheric environment was probed by various Mariner instruments.

Using a combination of data from the ultraviolet spectrometer, occultation results, and laboratory experiments, the Mariner 9 ultraviolet spectroscopy investigators were able to construct a model of the Martian ionosphere consistent with the hypothesis that all of the species present except atomic hydrogen are there as a direct or indirect result of the impingement of solar ultraviolet photons and electrons upon a pure CO_2 atmosphere. In their model, the temperature in the Martian ionosphere is in the region of 300° to 350° Kelvin, and the neutral species present, in order of their abundance, in addition to carbon dioxide, are atomic oxygen, carbon monoxide, and molecular oxygen. The primary ions present are O_2^+, CO_2^+, and O^+, in that order. (These represent, respectively, an oxygen molecule, a carbon dioxide molecule, and an oxygen atom, each of which has lost an electron.) At first glance, the relative abundances of molecular oxygen O_2 and the corresponding ion O_2^+ may seem inconsistent because O_2 is the least abundant neutral species and O_2^+ the most abundant ion. However, most of the O_2^+ is formed by a fast reaction between CO_2^+ and atomic oxygen; there is no direct dependence on the O_2 concentration. When either of the two major ions (O_2^+ or CO_2^+) recombines with an electron without a third particle present to absorb the energy released in the reaction, the recombined molecule wlil immediately dissociate into neutral particles with excess kinetic energy; these are the reactions that McElroy proposes to account for the loss of the oxygen initially produced by the photolysis of water vapor in the lower atmosphere of Mars.

That sufficient water vapor exists in the Mar-tian lower atmosphere to account for the hydrogen atom escape rate was confirmed by the infrared interferometer, which continuously monitored the water vapor content throughout the Mariner 9 mission. The infrared investigators found that the water vapor in the midlatitudinal regions remained fairly constant at 10 to 20 precipitable micrometers (the depth of the liquid layer that would result if all the water could be precipitated on the surface), while the concentration in the polar regions showed a strong seasonal effect. During the midsummer season in the southern hemisphere, the water vapor abundance in the south polar region was about the same as that in the midlatitudes, but no water vapor was observed in the north polar area. As the Martian seasons progressed to late spring in the northern hemisphere, 20 to 30 precipitable micrometers were detected over the north polar cap region, while the measurable water vapor in the southern polar area declined to zero. These measurements are consistent with the theory that at least some water vapor is frozen and trapped as water ice in the polar caps and seasonally transported between them. The total abundance of water vapor over the planet as determined by the infrared interferometer was considerably less than that measured from Earth in previous oppositions. The infrared investigators have suggested this may be due to adsorption of the vapor onto the dust particles during the planetwide dust storm. The data tend to support this hypothesis because the total abundance was observed to decrease as the dust settled and then increase once again as the surface warmed up.

In addition to water vapor, Mariner 9 also

showed that the temperature drop between 40° and 60° north latitude was extremely large, about 50° Celsius, so that the strong west winds inferred from the cloud structure and the temperature distribution were quite consistent with each other.

The small cloud wavelets that were observed usually appeared to be much closer to the surface. They may also have been formed by flow over topography, but there is no obvious relationship between these waves and surface features, and it is more likely that they are formed by overturning air at the interface between a slow-moving layer of air and a relatively rapidly moving higher one. Temperatures in the 45° to 55° north latitude zone were high enough that both the long wave clouds and the shorter cloud wavelets should have been made of water ice rather than carbon dioxide ice, and the infrared data showed that water ice was present in the region.

Day-to-day variations in northern clouds revealed fronts and large-scale storm systems like those that occur at middle and high latitudes on Earth. According to one of the investigators on the television experiment, a typical sequence of events was the following. The edge of the cloud pattern began north of its usual position, and was quite diffuse. Evidently, relatively warm air had been displaced unusually far north. Then the lee-wave activity began to intensify along the edge of the hood, and one or more broad bands of bright wave clouds formed, oriented from southwest to northeast, parallel to the wind. The most prominent band narrowed and began to move southeastward as the zone of strong temperature contrast became organized into a well-defined cold front. At this stage, the low-level short-wavelength clouds were widespread, and they often indicated northwesterly winds near the surface. On the northern side of the frontal cloud band, regular lines of clouds developed in the lowest 1 or 2 kilometers. These clouds were caused by heating of the very cold air as it moved southeastward over warmer ground and were probably made of carbon dioxide ice. (Clouds formed in a similar way are responsible for heavy snowfalls in some places on Earth, for example, around the Great Lakes, and it is possible that these clouds cause carbon dioxide snowfalls on Mars.) As the cold front moved southward, streamers in the carbon dioxide clouds behind the front showed marked curvature in the cyclonic (counterclockwise) sense, indicating the presence of a large low-pressure area in the cold air, perhaps 2000 to 4000 kilometers in diameter. As the front moved southward past 45° north latitude, the air behind it warmed and the clouds evaporated, but winds remained strong. On several occasions dust storms were observed in the 35° to 45° north latitude zone, apparently due to the strong surface winds behind such a cold front. The frontal cloud bands moved southeastward from 500 to 1000 kilometers per day. The entire process described above took about 2 or 3 days and was repeated at frequent intervals around the polar periphery.

Storm systems in terrestrial middle latitudes behave in a similar fashion, although they are a little longer lived and smaller in size than those on Mars appear to be. These storm systems are very effective in transferring heat and moisture to the polar regions. On Mars, this heat transfer

(Continued on page 135)

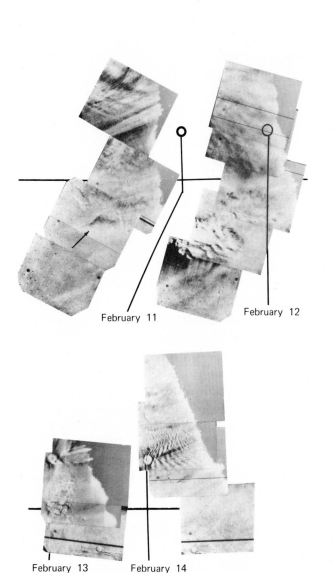

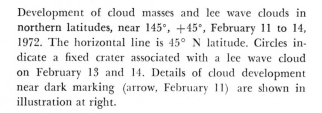

February 11   February 12

February 13   February 14

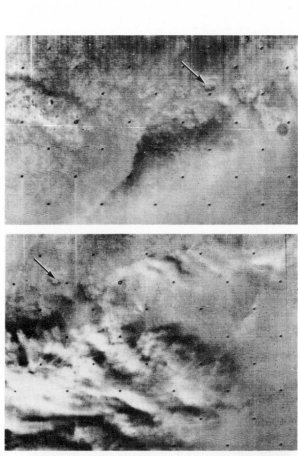

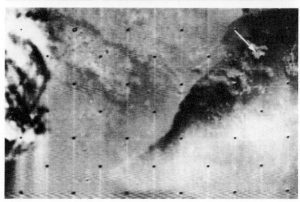

Development of cloud masses and lee wave clouds in **northern** latitudes, near 145°, +45°, February 11 to 14, 1972. The horizontal line is 45° N latitude. Circles indicate a fixed crater associated with a lee wave cloud on February 13 and 14. Details of cloud development near dark marking (arrow, February 11) are shown in illustration at right.

Cloud development near a dark region in Euxinus Lacus, near 158°, +38°. The arrow marks a fixed surface feature. These photographs were made on February 9, 12, and March 2. (P–12945)

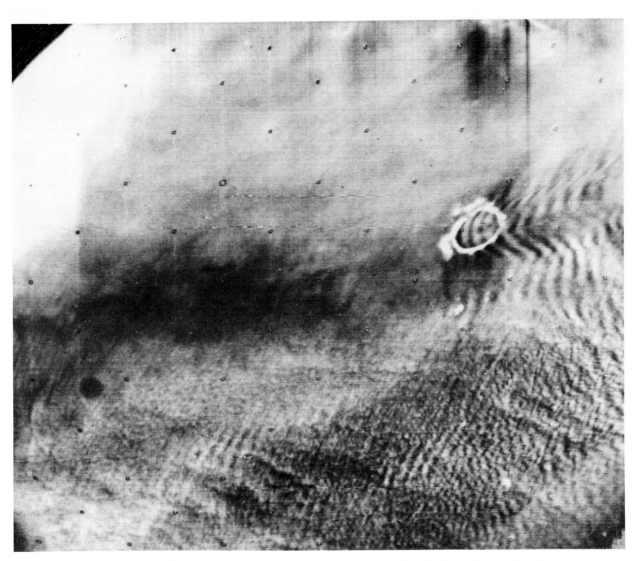

Scattered clouds and prominent lee wave cloud near a bright-rimmed (possibly the result of frost patches) crater at 72°, +55°. Wave spacing is about 30 kilometers. The long axis of frame covers about 900 kilometers. This photograph was made February 9, 1972; the prominent crater was free of wave clouds in photographs on February 27. (4208–90)

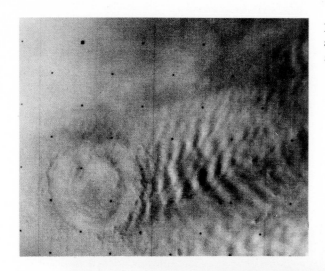

Details of wave cloud associated with a double-ring crater about 218 kilometers in diameter, near 327°, +52°. Waves are roughly 30 kilometers apart. (1649–125842)

Artist's conception of a lee wave cloud formed over a frost-rimmed crater seen from the Martian surface in the polar latitudes. (Painting by Ludek Pesek, © 1973, National Geographic Society)

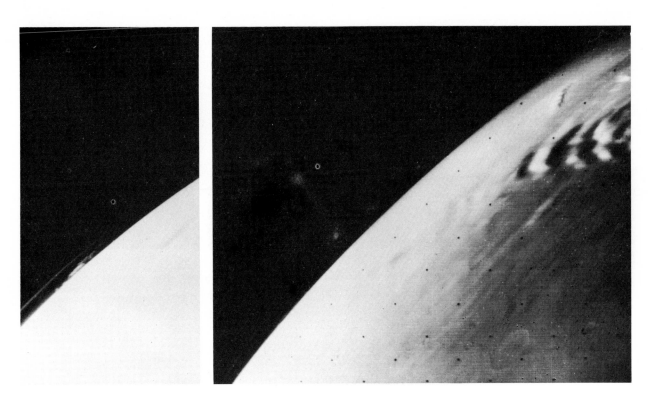

Two views of lee wave clouds over the Martian region of Tempe. Left view shows the clouds as billowy structures in profile on the horizon. The greatest heights are 30 kilometers; there is a thin dust layer at about 45 kilometers. Right view shows the wave clouds from above (upper right), where shadows suggest that they have a typical height of about 20 kilometers. (P–12795)

may well limit the rate at which carbon dioxide can freeze out onto the surface polar cap, and the moisture transfer rate may determine how much water is frozen out into the caps as they grow.

Not all of the condensation clouds observed were easily interpretable in terms of familiar terrestrial processes. As the northern summer progressed, a different type of cloud was seen to develop each afternoon over the west slopes of Olympus Mons and the three great calderas of the Tharsis dome. Clouds have often been seen in this region by astronomers, but the reason for their regular seasonal and diurnal occurrence remains a mystery. Infrared data showed the clouds to be made of ice crystals, and their seasonal appearance may coincide with the period when the water vapor released from the northern polar

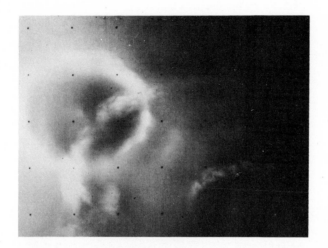
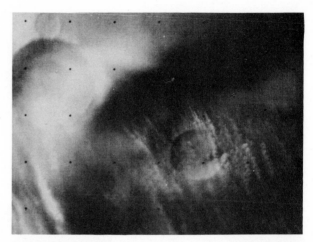

Telephoto views of clouds associated with craters. *Left*: February 11, 1972; near 347°, +63°, showing crater with rim apparently frost covered. *Right:* February 19, 1972; near 270°, +60°. (7063–160935, 1431–193240)

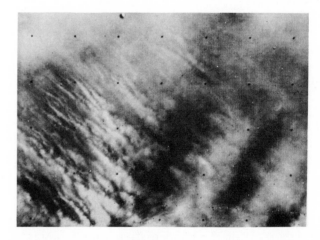

Telephoto views of cumuluslike clouds. In right view, filamentary streamers are a few kilometers apart. Both views were made February 28, 1972; photographs have similar scales. *Left:* near 177°, +54°. *Right:* near 178°, +60°. (1391–231015, 1391–232557)

cap reaches its maximum concentration in the atmosphere. The diurnal recurrence may be due to the daily heating and rising of this moist air up the slopes of the volcanoes. As previously mentioned, there may also be more water vapor in the atmosphere near the calderas than elsewhere.

Even more puzzling were some of the clouds observed near the retreating north polar cap during the summer. These long clouds, seen streaming off the cap toward the southwest, may have been due to water vapor subliming from the cap and recondensing in the atmosphere. They were quite unlike anything known in Earth's atmosphere.

At the turn of the century, when Lowell was writing, it was imagined that the Martian atmosphere might be like Earth's, which has a surface pressure of 1000 millibars. In 1909, Flammarion's book contained reasoning by the British astronomer Maunder leading to an estimated Martian surface pressure of 140 millibars. By the 1950's a number of techniques converged on a value around 85 millibars for the Martian surface pressure. As late as 1962, E. C. Slipher was able to comment that "numerical values reported for the surface pressure of Mars are remarkably concordant in spite of the many doubtful assumptions introduced." Slipher proposed a "most probable value" of 83 to 89 millibars, based on the various published results. At about the time of the Mariner 4 flight, new ground-based spectra lowered the estimated value to about 15 to 25 millibars. Within months, data from the Mariner 4 occultation experiment lowered the value still further to about 5 to 8 millibars. This value, less than 1 percent of Earth's surface pressure, has been confirmed by subsequent Mariner experiments and ground-based techniques. It means that the surface air density on Mars is equal to that at an altitude of 100 000 feet or more above Earth, an altitude three times that of most commercial jet flights. Thus Mars has been found to have an atmosphere much more rarefied than that assumed by early advocates of life on the planet.

Mariner 9, using data from the radio-occultation experiment and the two spectrometers on board the spacecraft, was able to accurately measure the surface pressure over most of the planet. The occultation experiment obtained 262 data points scattered over the entire surface, each of which provided an accurate pressure at that point. These pressures ranged in value from 2.8 millibars in the Cloritas and Tharsis areas to 10.3 millibars in the region of the north polar cap. It was then possible to normalize the spectrometer data to these points, resulting in a reasonably accurate surface pressure map covering most of the planet. The combined data indicated that some very low areas, such as the floor of Hellas or the bottom of the Vallis Marineris, may have pressures as high as 12 millibars or more. Recalling that the triple-point pressure above which liquid water can exist is 6.1 millibars, it appears there are many areas on Mars low enough to sustain liquid water provided it becomes available under temperature conditions high enough to prevent freezing.

The determination of the topographic shape of Mars, both from atmospheric and other information, raises the possibility of determining information about the internal structure of the planet. This information will be considered in the next chapter.

CHAPTER XI

The Shape and Global Geology of Mars

The planet Mars holds out the best possibility of testing the hypothesis that the inner planets can be regarded as having similar compositions, since it possesses satellites and therefore more can be known of its internal mass-distribution than is the case for either Venus or Mercury. Even so, it appears that neither the radius nor mass of Mars has yet been determined with the [needed] accuracy. . . .

— R. A. Lyttleton, 1963

The previous chapters have discussed the conditions on and near the surface of Mars, both now and in the past. However, Mariner 9 discoveries were not restricted to the surface; they reflected on both the interior and external environment of Mars. For example, the motions of the spacecraft directly indicate the form of the gravitational field around the planet, which is in turn shaped by the mass distribution inside Mars. A topographic bulge on one side of Mars or a concentration of dense material under the surface in one area would distort the gravity field and alter the spacecraft's motion as it passed over that area. Discovery of such motions would imply geologic anomalies that might be seen in the surface structure revealed by photographs. Thus Mariner 9 data on the gravity field, the topography, and the surface geologic units all have a complex relationship.

For many years it has been suspected that Mars is not precisely spherical in shape but rather flattened at the poles like Earth. Direct optical measurements of the shape of the disk have been attempted by astronomers over the past 100 years. These attempts ran into several problems, such as the fuzziness of the image and different results with red and blue light, due to their different sensitivities to the Martian atmosphere. Nonetheless, positive results were obtained: the equatorial radius was found to be about 36 kilometers greater than the radius at the poles. This flattening, or oblateness, is usually expressed in terms of the ratio $(r_e - r_p) / r_e$, where r_e is the equatorial radius and r_p the radius at the pole. For Mars it was found to be approximately 0.011.

Unfortunately, two serious problems with this result were apparent at once: it was well above the theoretical limit for flattening if Mars were a homogeneous planet and it was also twice that obtained from an independent measurement, known as dynamic flattening. Whereas optical flattening is associated with the visual or geometric shape of a planet, dynamic flattening is a calculated value determined from the gravitational field; it is a measure of the total mass distribution within the planet. If a planet has a natural satellite in a closed orbit, the effect of a nonspherical gravitational field on the orbital movement of this satellite will allow a determination of the dynamic flattening. Both of Mars' moons are close to the planet, and calculations based on studies of their orbital motions resulted in a value of 0.0052 for the dynamic flattening; these discrepant results led to some controversy. However, H. C. Urey pointed out in 1950 that the two observations could be brought into accord if there were a ring of high mountainous terrain in the equatorial

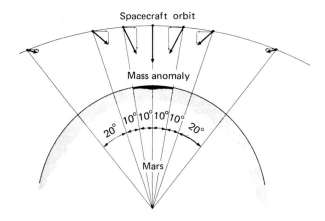

Schematic diagram showing gravitational effects of a surface mass anomaly on the motion of the spacecraft orbiting Mars.

zone, isostatically compensated by a layer of less dense material beneath the mountains. Such high terrain could be responsible for the optically observed oblateness without affecting the validity of the dynamic flattening measurements.

Data from the Mariner 9 radio-occultation experiment determined that the equatorial radius was about 19 kilometers greater than the polar radius, and the photographs indicated low-latitude uplifted volcanic domes in Tharsis and Elysium. At the same time, the Mariner 9 celestial mechanics data verified the value for dynamic flattening derived from the motion of the Martian satellites. Data from both of these experiments also indicated quite early in the mission that the shape of Mars was much more complex than anyone had anticipated.

After the first orbital trim of Mariner 9, tracking data revealed that its orbital period was not constant but was oscillating sinusoidally in

18-day cycles. This behavior indicated that Mars was not only meridionally but also equatorially noncircular in shape—a result unanticipated by the Mariner scientists. Analysis of the tracking data by the occultation and celestial mechanics teams showed that the long axis of the equator ran through the Tharsis region, site of the high volcanoes. Tracking data also showed that this region represented a gravity anomaly 17 times greater than any observed on Earth. Apparently the slowly acting tectonic forces that shattered the crust and produced the volcanism in the Tharsis area also contributed to an irregularly shaped planet. Thus, in geometric terms, the shape of Mars is somewhat better defined by a triaxial ellipsoid than the oblate spheroid representative of Earth's shape.

Analysis of several different measurements of the shape of Mars, such as ultraviolet spectroscopy altimetry and radar data, gives values for the radius of Mars through three axes. March 1973 averages are as follows: the longest equatorial axis (105° longitude), 3396 kilometers; the equatorial axis at right angles to the longest equatorial axis, 3394 kilometers; and the polar axis, 3376 kilometers. It will be noted that the longest equatorial axis lies on a line through the longitudes of Syrtis Major and the highly elevated Tharsis region.

The Mariner 9 occultation data revealed still another anomaly in the shape of the planet: averaging over large regions the northern polar area was found to be lower (closer to the Martian center of mass) than the southern polar area by an average of about 3.4 kilometers. However, some investigators suggested that the surfaces of the northern and southern polar layered

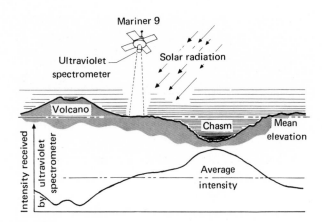

Schematic illustration showing correlation between Martian relief and light intensity received by ultraviolet spectroscopy experiment, which measures ultraviolet light scattered by the Martian atmosphere.

deposits were at about the same altitude, indicating that the layered deposits were considerably thicker at the northern pole. The additional burden represented by this increased thickness is consistent with the hypothesis, mentioned in an earlier chapter, that regional tectonic readjustment may have occurred in the north after the laminated deposits formed, accommodating their weight. Data on the absolute altitudes in layered terrain are relatively poor and this problem will bear further study.

As described earlier, both infrared and ultraviolet spectral instruments aboard Mariner 9 gathered data concerning the Martian surface pressure, which can be converted to topographical information by use of barometric equations with suitable corrections. These data tie together the widely spaced but more geometrically direct occultation measurements of topography and add a striking third dimension to the Martian map. To obtain such data, the infrared spectrometer made use of the absorption properties of carbon dioxide, the principal constituent in Mars' atmosphere. By monitoring the strength of CO_2 absorption features, infrared interferometer spectrometer analysts were able to measure the changes in total carbon dioxide density and convert them to altitude differences correlated with topographical features in the instrument's field of view. This method was limited to some extent by its sensitivity to atmospheric temperature, requiring careful and detailed analysis of each spectrum. The ultraviolet spectroscopy technique was somewhat easier, being based on scattering properties of the atmosphere, which are temperature independent. Molecules in the Martian atmosphere cause Rayleigh scattering, a strong effect at ultraviolet wavelengths. Measurements of the amount of Rayleigh scattering at ultraviolet wavelengths indicate the amount of atmospheric gas in the line of sight, and hence the elevation of the ground, in terms of a reference level. By choosing a narrow-wavelength region in the ultraviolet portion of the spectrum that was free of any absorption or emission features, ultraviolet spectroscopy analysts were able to correlate the measured intensities with the topography as viewed by the television cameras.

Additional topographical information was obtained from the Mariner 9 data by the use of stereoscopic techniques. Obtaining stereoscopic coverage of the Martian surface was not a specific objective of the Mariner 9 mission, but during the great dust storm many pictures were taken from different viewing angles of the few

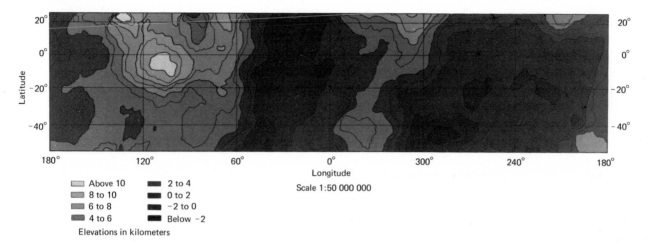

Elevations in kilometers

Above 10		2 to 4	
8 to 10		0 to 2	
6 to 8		−2 to 0	
4 to 6		Below −2	

Scale 1:50 000 000

Martian topography determined by the ultraviolet spectroscopy experiment showing the high Tharsis volcanic area (left) and depressed Hellas basin (lower right) as prominent features. (University of Colorado)

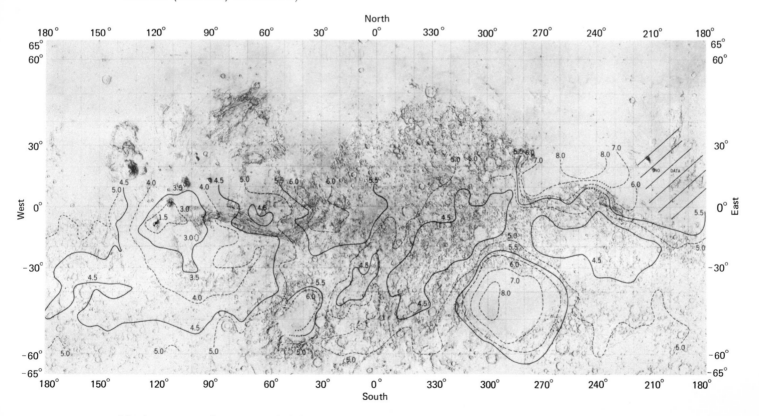

Martian topography, as revealed by pressure contours (numbers indicate millibars of atmospheric pressure), based on infrared spectrometer results. Highest pressures, exceeding 8 millibars, occur in the floor of the Hellas basin and near the Moeris Lacus basin. Low pressures occur on the Tharsis volcanic dome.

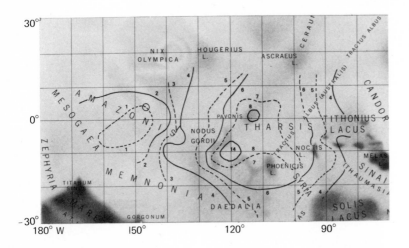

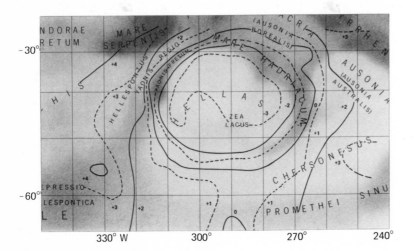

Detailed Martian topography in the highest (Tharsis, *top*) and lowest (Hellas basin, *bottom*) areas showing estimated elevation contours in kilometers, referenced to the 6.1-millibar pressure level in the atmosphere, based on infrared spectrometer results.

surface features that were relatively unobscured, such as the huge volcanoes and the south polar cap. Using computer techniques, the Mariner 9 scientists were able to rectify and scale many of these images into satisfactory stereopairs from which relief information could be obtained by photogrammetry. In spite of less-than-ideal pairs of images, there was reasonable agreement between the altitudes thus obtained and the measurements made by the spectrometers. For example, after refinement all methods converged on a height of Olympus Mons in excess of 20 kilometers.

Having mapped and measured the shape and topography of Mars with a resolution at least 20 times better than obtained by the best Earth-based photographs, there remained the task for the Mariner 9 scientists to make a commensurate improvement in the definition of the Martian coordinate system used to make maps and locate features on the surface of the planet. The observers Beer and Mädler in 1840 and Proctor in 1867 chose a certain dark feature as marking the prime meridian on their pioneering maps. Schiaparelli retained this choice in his influential map of 1877, and he named it "Meridiani Sinus." This longitude line, defined by the center of Sinus Meridiani, was equivalent to the Greenwich Observatory meridian on Earth. As improvements were made in the ephemeris of Mars, which defines the planet's motions, this definition became harder to maintain. Errors in the rotational period necessitated frequent adjustments in the ephemeris. Finally, in 1909 the decision was made to redefine the prime meridian of Mars by assigning a central meridian longitude as seen from Earth at a chosen epoch,

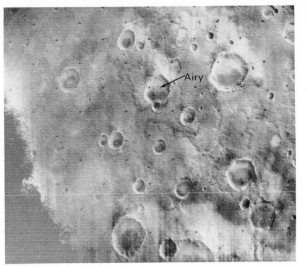
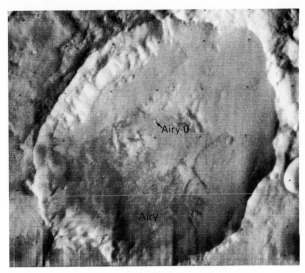

The newly defined position of the Martian prime meridian of longitude, passing through the crater Airy-0, named after the astronomer who defined the prime meridian of Earth.

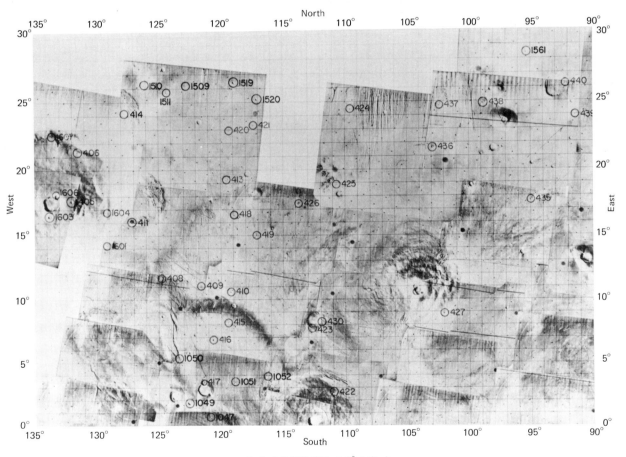

Scale 1:5 000 000 at 0° latitude

Examples of points identified for use in the control net defining Martian latitude and longitude. These points (circles) are mostly small craters in the Tharsis volcanic region.

adopting the best known rotation period, and predicting the central meridian's longitude at each future instant of time. Thus the prime meridian was defined by the ephemeris itself rather than a fixed surface feature and allowed to drift as necessary to compensate for errors in the rotational period of the planet.

With the greatly improved knowledge of the ephemeris, rotational period, and pole positions, the Mariner 9 scientists recommended that the 0° meridian once more be defined by a fixed topographic feature, just as on Earth. The center of a small, nearly circular crater lying near the center of the Sinus Meridiani area was chosen as the Martian Greenwich. The small crater chosen lies within a larger crater easily seen on wide-angle pictures taken by both Mariners 6 and 9. Thus the known areographic relationship between the progressively larger terrain features allows the prime meridian to be accurately located at any resolution, including Earth-based resolution. The Mariner 9 scientists recommended that the larger crater be named Airy and the small crater Airy-0 in honor of Sir George Biddell Airy, who, during his tenure as director of Greenwich Observatory from 1835 to 1881, installed the transit instrument that was used to define the 0° meridian on Earth.

Thus Mariner 9 not only refined our data on the geometric shape of Mars but also laid the cartographic groundwork for future maps of the planet.

Analysis of Mariner 9 data will also clarify the significance of the shape of Mars. For example the motions of the spacecraft revealed irregularities in the gravitational field that indicated irregularities in the internal structure of the planet. Comparison of the gravity measurements to the geometric shape revealed whether the assumed masses of the Tharsis dome and other bulges were sufficient to account for their large positive-gravity anomalies, or whether additional mass or density concentrations were needed. Preliminary analysis of the gravity data suggested that density irregularities exist under the Tharsis region and that perhaps new crustal rock was being added there at the interface between the Martian mantle and crust. No precise analogs have been found to match lunar "mascons," the broad, flat mass concentrations associated with the lava plains of the Moon; in this sense the Martian crustal mass irregularities are uniquely Martian.

As for the deep interior structure of Mars, it was realized some decades ago that the presence of an internal iron core—like that surmised for Earth—could be tested if sufficiently accurate mass, radius, and related data were available. Such a test would help indicate the similarity or differences between Earth and Mars. As indicated by the quotation from R. A. Lyttleton, this problem was still in doubt as late as 1963. Data from the early Mariners in 1965 and 1969 increased the precision of the mass and radius determinations. As a result, studies by theorists such as D. Anderson, A. Binder, and D. Davis have indicated that Mars does have a substantial dense core. The new data from Mariner 9 will help clarify the dimensions and density of this core and thus shed light on its composition and evolutionary significance. Assumptions have been made in the past about the melting of planetary interiors and the resulting concentration of iron in their centers, but recent studies of the Moon as well as Mars have raised questions about the sequence of temperature changes and chemical differentiation. These questions are now open, but it is widely believed that comparative data on Martian and other cases may produce a new understanding of the structural evolution of planets.

Mariner 9 mapping of shape and gravity irregularities of Mars led to better interpretation of the surface geology than could have been possible from the pictures alone. For example, the knowledge that Tharsis and Elysium are elevated and the measurement of the depths of the Vallis Marineris or the Hellas basin help to sort out physical and structural characteristics of these terrain units from superficial characteristics such as dark veneers of dust. After review and synthesis of the photographs and other data, Mariner 9 geologists have named 4 broad categories of units and 14 types of specific geological units.

Unit	Map abbreviation
(1) Densely cratered:	
(a) Cratered deposits, undivided (ancient surface)	cu
(b) Cratered deposits, mantled (ancient areas with younger deposits)	cm
(c) Mountainous deposits (rims of large basins)	m
(2) Plains-forming materials (generally volcanic and eolian):	
(a) Heavily cratered plains material (old lava plains)	pc
(b) Moderately cratered plains material (Tharsis and Elysium lavas)	pm
(c) Sparsely cratered plains materials (very young Tharsis and other lavas)	ps
(d) Mottled cratered plains materials (polar plains with eolian deposits)	pp
(3) Volcanic (excluding plains-forming units):	
(a) Volcanic materials (shield volcanoes, domes, etc.)	v
(b) Grooved terrain materials, coarse (near Nix Olympica, fractured?)	gc
(c) Grooved terrain materials, fine (from Nix Olympica)	gf
(4) Other:	
(a) Channel deposits (riverbedlike deposits)	ch
(b) Channel deposits (floor of Vallis Marineris, for example)	y
(c) Chaotic deposits (low, collapsed (?) units)	h
(d) Knobby deposits ("fretted" terrain, isolated hills)	k

These units are used to divide the map of Mars into geologic provinces for more detailed study. They represent a finer subdivision than employed in the earlier chapters, where we noted such terrain types as cratered terrain, volcanic units, chaotic terrain, and channels.

The densely cratered and plains-forming units can be thought of as characterizing the two dissimilar hemispheres of Mars, mentioned earlier in this book. The other two groups of units contain the isolated, somewhat anomalous features, such as large volcanoes, channels, and chaotic terrain.

These units can be arranged in a stratigraphic age sequence based on estimated relative ages and related to Martian processes, as shown in the following diagram:

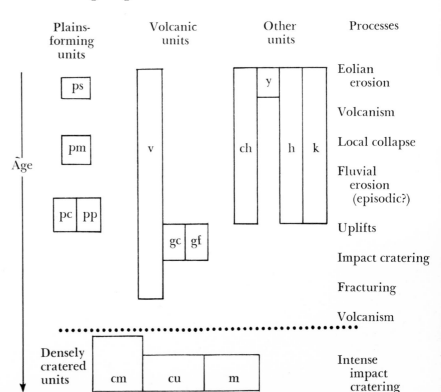

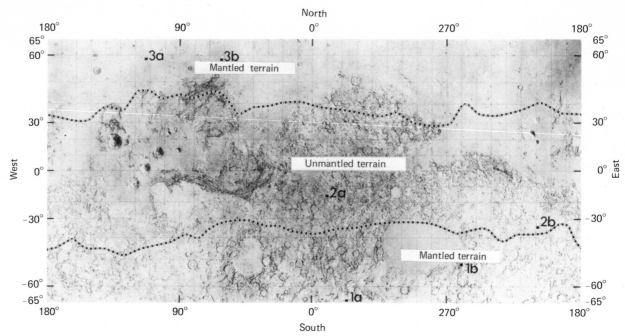

Example of simplified mapping of geologic units (mantled versus unmantled terrain) on the airbrush map of Martian structural features. Mantled units occur at high latitudes and probably result from transport of dust to polar regions.

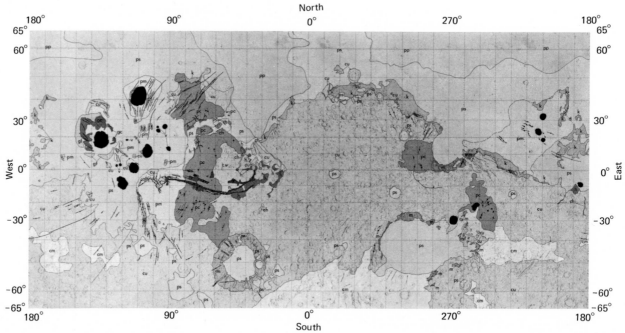

Geologic map of Mars, showing distribution of geologic provinces discussed in the text. This map is a synthesis of a great variety of Mariner 9 data and analyses. (U.S. Geological Survey)

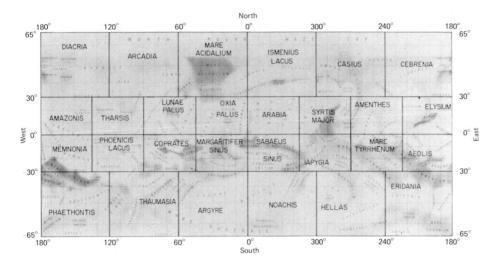

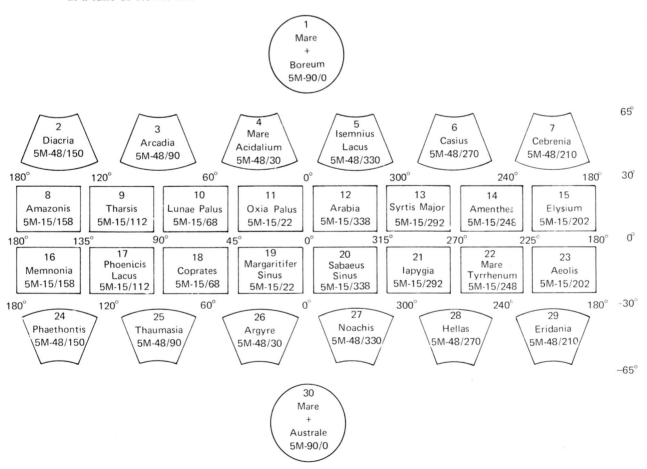

Proposed division of Mars into "quadrangles" for detailed mapping program, superimposed on map of classic features.

Numbering and shapes of quadrangles proposed for mapping program to produce maps at a scale of 1:5 000 000.

The story told by this diagram is the history of Mars, sketched in rough outline. Looking at the present planet we see the results of the current dust storms and the results of relatively recent processes such as the lava flows and volcanism near Olympus Mons, the production of chaotic terrain, and the formation of the channels at a time when more water may have been available. At an earlier time, fracturing must have occurred, as well as early volcanism, that gave rise to the major canyons, fault patterns, and lava plains. Throughout this period and stretching back to the earliest eras, meteorite impacts created craters as Mars swept up debris from interplanetary space. The most densely cratered units contain the earliest surviving record, but even they have ben altered by Martian erosion and other localized disturbances.

To search for the least-altered evidence of early processes involving Mars, we need to escape from the influence of the Martian atmosphere and internal evolutionary processes. Fortunately, nature has provided two small satellites above the Martian atmosphere, and these may contain clues to very ancient events, as described in the next chapter.

CHAPTER XII

Phobos and Deimos

[*The astronomers of Laputa*] *have . . . discovered two lesser stars, or satellites, which revolve about Mars, whereof the innermost is distant from the center of the primary planet exactly three of his diameters and the outermost five . . .*
> —DEAN SWIFT, 1720, in *Gulliver's Travels*

. . . [five German mariners setting forth] to find out whether it is true that on July 10 of this year [1744] the planet Mars appeared with a satellite or moon for the first time since the world has been in existence.
> —EBERHARD CHRISTIAN KINDERMANN, 1744, IN *Die Geschwinde Reise auf dem Lufft-Schiff nach obern Welt,* QUOTED BY MARJORIE NICOLSON

. . . our travelers crossed a space of about a hundred million leagues and reached the planet Mars. They saw two moons which wait on this planet, and which have escaped the gaze of astronomers. I know well that l'abbé Castrel wrote against the existence of these two moons; but I agree with those who reason from analogy. These good philosophers know how difficult it would be for Mars, which is so far from the Sun, to get on with less than two moons.
> —VOLTAIRE, 1750, IN *Micromégas*

. . . at half past two o'clock [August 11, 1877] I found a faint object on the following side and a little north of the planet, which afterward proved to be the outer satellite. I had hardly time to secure an observation of its position when fog from the Potomac River stopped the work.
> —ASAPH HALL, 1877, ON THE DISCOVERY OF THE MARTIAN SATELLITES

After years of searching by various astronomers Asaph Hall finally discovered satellites near Mars at the Naval Observatory in Washington in 1877. There were two of them and they were small bodies, too faint to be seen by such earlier astronomers as Herschel, who had searched for satellites as early as 1783. Careful reading of the quotations above reveal the curious fact that literary writers were alluding to the two moons of Mars 150 years before they were discovered. This coincidence, which would seem to belong in a book on astrology, can be explained through further historical research. Johann Kepler, who discovered the laws of planetary motion about 1610, was something of a believer in numerology or, as he called it, the harmony of the spheres. When the telescopic observations of Galileo revealed that Jupiter, the next planet beyond Mars, had four satellites, Kepler and others speculated about the possibility of Martian satellites. The argument went that, in order out from the Sun, Venus had no moons, Earth had one, Mars was uncertain, and Jupiter had four. Two moons for Mars seemed the proper assumption to fit the mathematical progression.

This speculation was probably read by Swift (who is known to have been familiar with Kepler's laws) and Voltaire, who worked it into their fiction. As for Swift's prediction of the orbital distances being three and five Martian diameters, the correct numbers as discovered by Hall are about 1.4 and 3.5 Mars diameters.

After Hall discovered the satellites, a number of possible names were suggested, but Hall chose a suggestion by Madan, of Eton, England, who noted in Greek mythology and in Homer that the two horses drawing the chariot of the god of war were Phobos (fear) and Deimos (terror).

Knowing the brightness of the Martian satellites, pre-Mariner astronomers could assume various reflectivities for the Martian satellites and thus compute how big they had to be to reflect the observed amount of light. Assumed reflectivities were those of the Moon, meteorites, or terrestrial rocks. These led to early estimates of Phobos' and Deimos' diameters, respectively, of about 49 and 32 kilometers (30 and 20 miles). The two moons were hardly more than floating mountains. Later Earth-based estimates revised the figures to values as low as 16 and 8 kilometers (10 and 5 miles).

Because these two satellites appear only as faint points of light nearly lost in the glare of nearby Mars, little could be learned about their nature. It was widely assumed that their presence and their unusually small size, unique among the nearby planets, might have something to do with the nearness of Mars to the asteroid belt, which is composed of countless similar objects ranging in size from large asteroids a few hundred kilometers in diameter to many objects smaller than Phobos or Deimos.

In 1969, Mariner 7 obtained a photograph of Mars in which Phobos was silhouetted against the planet. This was the first detection of the disk of Phobos allowing a direct measurement of the size of the satellite. Phobos was found to be irregular in shape with dimensions of about 18 by 22 kilometers and an unusually dark surface. The image was so small and dark that no craters or other surface detail could be seen.

Early in the Mariner 9 mission a similar image of Phobos in silhouette was obtained, but this was of only passing interest when compared to the high-resolution closeup photographs of both Phobos and Deimos that were later to come from the mission. Because of the obscuration of the surface of Mars by the dust storm, a substantial part of the photographic picture budget was applied to the satellites during early weeks of the mission.

First the satellites had to be reliably located, using the best determinations of their orbits available from Earth-based studies. Searches for the satellites and their eventual acquisition by the telephoto camera resulted in improvements to the earlier knowledge of their orbits. For example, a 600-kilometer (3°) correction was made to the mean longitude of Phobos in its orbit, and the inclination of its orbit was corrected by 0.3°.

Once the satellites were acquired by the telephoto camera, there was much excitement over

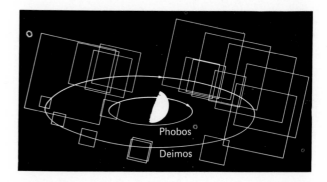

Mariner 9's preorbital pictures of the vicinity of Martian satellite orbits. These frames, mapped here against the orbits of Phobos and Deimos, were used to acquire the two satellites and to search for new satellites.

their appearance. Until that moment, no one had known what the surface of an asteroidal-sized body would look like. Would it be polished smooth by countless micrometeorite impacts acting like a sandblasting process? Or would it be pitted with large craters? Would there be a layer of dust, as on the Moon? Or would the dust have been knocked off by impacts, exposing bare rock? Would the surface be coherent or highly fractured? Could it be proven that the satellites were rocky, or could they possibly be metallic (as are iron meteorites) or even loose, sandy agglomerations of particles? Lurking in the back of investigators' minds was a hypothesis advanced a few years ago by the Soviet scientist I. Shklovskii, who reasoned from certain unusual characteristics of Phobos' orbit that it might be an artificial satellite launched by a Martian civilization. (Some of the assumed orbital peculiarities on which this hypothesis had been based had been discounted by the time of the Mariner 9 mission, so the idea was scarcely viable.)

The first telephoto photographs of Phobos and Deimos revealed them to be heavily cratered bodies with about as many craters per unit area as the most densely cratered parts of the Moon. This discovery, supported by numerical calculations of crater formation rates, indicated that Phobos and Deimos are probably billions of years old and may date back to the formation of Mars.

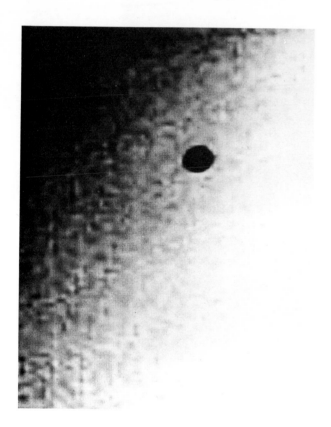

Phobos, silhouetted against Mars, in a preorbital view by Mariner 9 taken about 150 000 kilometers from Phobos. (P–12679)

Phobos was observed by the infrared radiometer on board Mariner 9 as it emerged from the eclipses produced when it passed through the shadow of Mars. Measurements of the temperature as Phobos passed into sunlight indicated the rate of warming of the satellite surfaces and hence allowed an estimate of the amount of insulating dust on the surface. It was found that the satellites have a very thin layer of dust, perhaps millimeters thick. This evidence was supported by University of Arizona astronomer Ben Zellner, who, at about the same time, obtained polarization measures of Deimos with Earth-based telescopes indicating that the surface of Deimos was not bare rock, but had a dust cover.

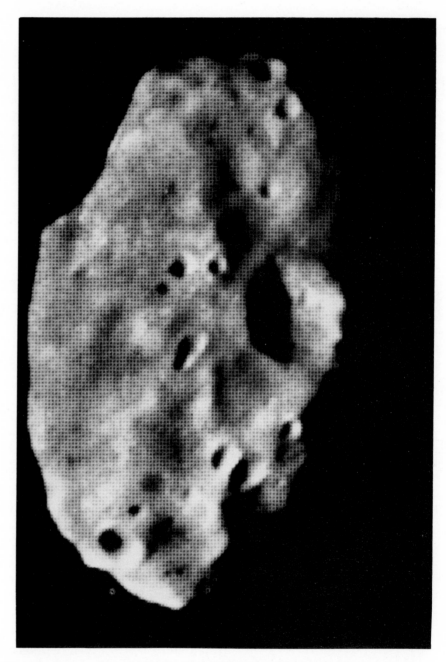

The first closeup view of Phobos, from 5720 kilometers, showing the satellite's cratered surface. The largest visible crater is about 5 kilometers in diameter. The "notch" in the edge of Phobos, upper left, is the site of a larger crater, about 9 kilometers in diameter. Phase angle (Sun-Phobos-spacecraft), 59°. (83–235921)

Phobos. The largest visible crater is about 5 kilometers in diameter. Somewhat below it, middle right, is an alinement of small craters, which may mark an internal fracture in Phobos. Range, 6460 kilometers; phase angle, 57°. (DAS 4 215 690)

The fact that Phobos and Deimos display discrete impact craters and retain some dust produced during these impacts places interesting and useful constraints on our knowledge of what happens when small interplanetary bodies collide in space. The results cannot be extrapolated directly to asteroids, however, because dust knocked off Phobos and Deimos remains in orbit around Mars and can be swept up by them later, as shown by Berkeley dynamicist Steven Soter.

Measurements of the Mariner 9 pictures have revealed the sizes and shapes of the two satellites. Preliminary measurements show that the satellites can be thought of as roughly potato shaped, with three main axes having the following diameters:

	Phobos	Deimos
Longest diameter, kilometers	28	16
Intermediate diameter, kilometers	23	12
Shortest diameter, kilometers	20	10

For each of these measurements, the estimated probable error is about 1 kilometer. Because the shapes are so irregular, another way of expressing the satellite sizes is to give the diameter of a sphere having the same projected area as the average projected area of the satellites. For Phobos the diameter of the equivalent sphere would be 21.8 kilometers; for Deimos, the diameter would be 11.4 kilometers. Thus the two satellites are indeed "flying mountains," about 14 and 8 miles in diameter.

Dynamic studies of elongated satellites by scientists such as Joseph Burns of Cornell University and Steven Soter of the University of California at Berkeley indicated prior to the Mariner 9 mission that they should be alined by tidal forces so that their long axes point toward the primary planet. The same is true for Earth's Moon, which explains the fact that it keeps one face toward Earth at all times. Detailed photography of the surface features of these satellites permitted Mariner 9 scientists to test this prediction and it was found to be correct. Phobos and Deimos keep one side toward Mars at all times. This indicates that no large impact has disrupted the tidal locking or set the moons to spinning within the last 100 million years or so.

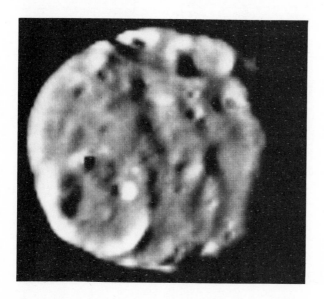

The 8-kilometer crater, largest on Phobos, is prominent in the lower left in this view from 10 400 kilometers; phase angle, 45°. (1581–114434)

Both Phobos and Deimos have very dark surfaces, as dark as the darker regions of the Moon. This low reflectivity is equivalent to that of dark basaltic lavas or certain types of very primitive meteorites (carbonaceous chondrites) and darker than Mars or such terrestrially familiar rocks as granite.

The fact that Phobos and Deimos have been struck by many crater-forming meteorites leads to the idea that they might be highly fractured internally. The largest clear crater on Phobos is about 8 kilometers in diameter, which approaches the radius of Phobos itself; obviously Phobos could not have sustained a much larger impact without being blown apart. The energy required to form the 8-kilometer crater is believed to be about 10^{25} to 10^{26} ergs, equivalent to 10 000 to 100 000 atomic bombs of the Hiroshima size, or equivalent to perhaps 1000 bombs of megaton size. Mariner scientists have analyzed the effect of this energy dissipation in Phobos and the probability of Phobos' withstanding impacts of still larger size. From these studies it appears that Phobos (and presumably Deimos) must be composed of relatively well-consolidated material; it is believed that this material is probably rock interlaced with fractures caused by the impacts.

All of these discoveries and conjectures about Phobos and Deimos—perhaps seemingly unrelated—point back to the early history of the solar system, because they all suggest that the satellites have been cratered for a long time and have not been recently captured or disturbed. What, then, is the origin of these two small moons? A direct attack on this question leads to frustrations. For example, the simplest idea, that they are merely captured asteroids, encounters difficulties because of the satellites' orbits. Captured bodies would be expected to have rather "irregular orbits"—i.e., with high eccentricities and/or high inclination to the plane of Mars' equator. Yet Phobos and Deimos have circular orbits lying in the plane of Mars' equator. Dynamicist S. Fred Singer has shown that such orbits might result from tidal forces, but only if the satellites were hundreds of times more massive than Phobos or Deimos. Alternatively, one could invoke a whole swarm of minisatellites that, through collisions, would cause drag forces that might produce such orbits, but then one is faced with the problem of accounting for the present whereabouts of the minisatellites.

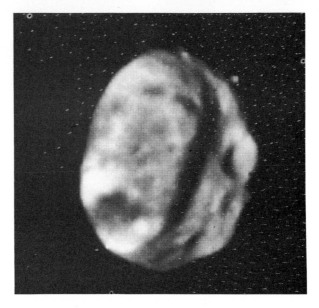

View from a perspective somewhat different from the view on the facing page, showing the lateral valley or scarp on Phobos. Range, 12 500 kilometers; phase angle, 18°. (1570–163600)

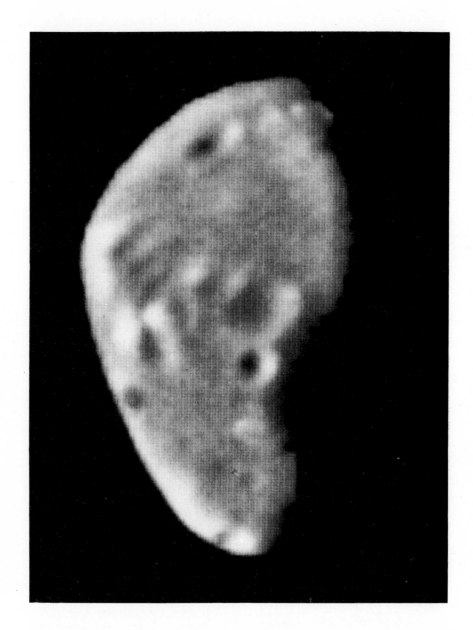

The closest available photograph of Deimos, from 5470 kilometers. The phase angle is 65°. Several craters ranging up to about 2 kilometers in diameter can be seen. (1599–201122)

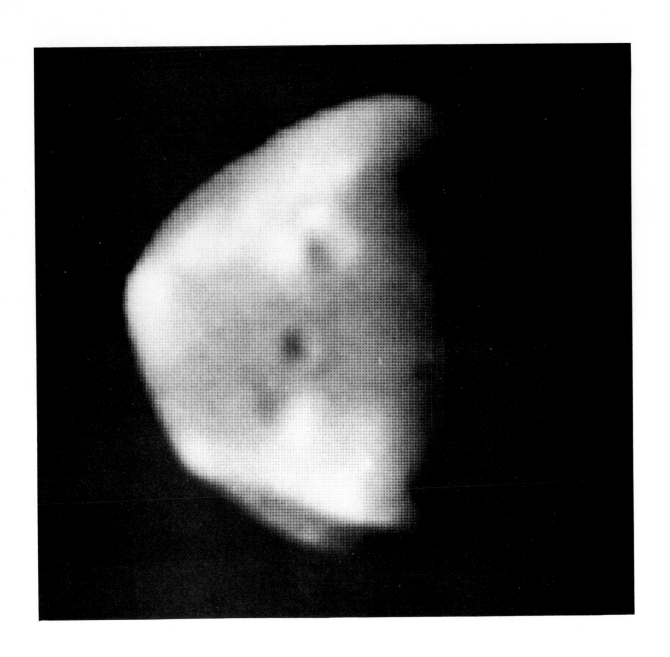

Deimos, seen from 7780 kilometers and with phase angle 73°.
Note saddle-shaped valley at bottom edge. (951–220924)

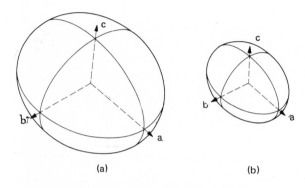

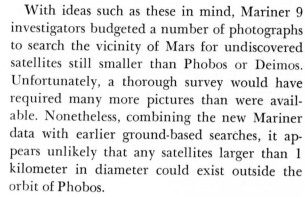

Orientations of Phobos (*a*) and Deimos (*b*) represented as triaxial ellipsoids. (*a* = longest axis, toward Mars; *b* = intermediate axis, in orbit plane; *c* = shortest axis, normal to orbit plane.)

With ideas such as these in mind, Mariner 9 investigators budgeted a number of photographs to search the vicinity of Mars for undiscovered satellites still smaller than Phobos or Deimos. Unfortunately, a thorough survey would have required many more pictures than were available. Nonetheless, combining the new Mariner data with earlier ground-based searches, it appears unlikely that any satellites larger than 1 kilometer in diameter could exist outside the orbit of Phobos.

Another idea about the origin of Phobos and Deimos is that they might have formed in equatorial orbits around Mars using a cloud of finely

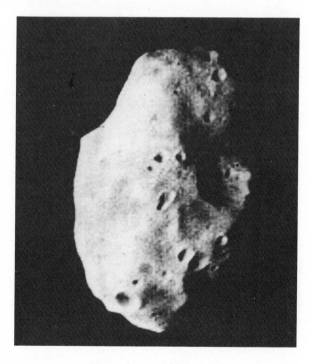

Two views of Phobos from a direction within 20° of Phobos' south pole. The reproducibility between this and other pairs of pictures shows that Phobos is locked in synchronous rotation with Mars, as the Moon is with Earth. (820–00205, 937–103305)

dispersed material similar to that which is widely thought to have formed the Moon and many other satellites of the solar system. One unanswered problem in this theory is that if the process was similar to that producing other satellites, why are Phobos and Deimos only a millionth as massive as the supposedly analogous satellites. Another problem is that Phobos and possibly Deimos display valleylike depressions and irregularities of form that would not be expected if they were the direct products of accretion from innumerable tiny bodies. If they are such satellites, they must have been substantially deformed by many impacts subsequent to formation.

Still another idea, favored in a recently published report by Mariner analysts, is that Phobos and Deimos represent fragments of an initially larger satellite. This would be consistent, for example, with their similarity in having unusu-

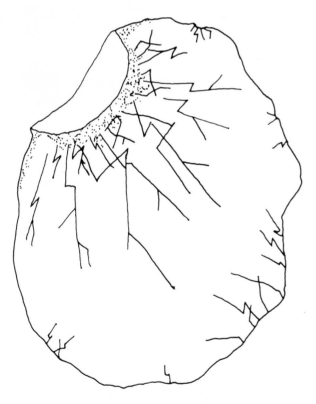

Hypothetical cross section through the 8-kilometer crater on Phobos, showing fractures beneath the crater and at the antipodal point, based on laboratory experiments with rock samples.

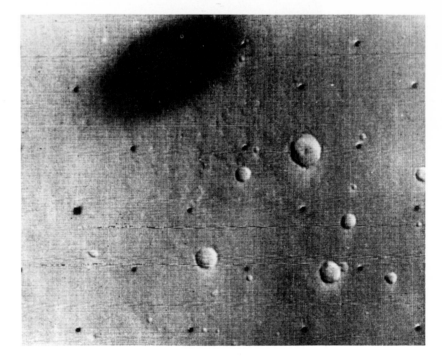

A solar eclipse occurring on Mars. The shadow of Phobos is seen here falling on the Aethiopis region, February 4, 1972. The penumbral shadow measures about 50 by 110 kilometers. An observer inside the shadow would see an annular eclipse, with Phobos passing across, and obscuring part of, the Sun. (P–12868)

Phobos and Mars, showing the cratered satellite, the Martian canyonlands, and the volcano Ascraeus Mons. (Painting by Don Davis, 1972, courtesy of the U.S. Geological Survey and Morrison Planetarium, San Francisco)

APPENDIX B

Mariner 9 Television Science Discipline and Task Groups

TEAM LEADERS: H. MASURSKY AND B. SMITH

SCIENCE DISCIPLINE GROUPS

Atmospheric Phenomena

*Leovy, C.
  Briggs, G. (1)
  Shipley, E. (1)
  Smith, B. (1)
  Wildey, R. (2)
  Pollack, J. (3)
  Young, A. (3)

Geodesy/Cartography

*de Vaucouleurs, G.
  Arthur, D. (1)
  Batson, R. (1)
  Borgeson, W. (1)
  Davies, M. (1)
  Leighton, R. (2)
  Young, A. (2)
  Wildey, R. (3)

Geology

*McCauley, J.
  Carr, M. (1)
  Hartmann, W. (1)
  Sharp, R. (1)
  Soderblom, L. (1)
  Wilhelms, D. (1)
  Cutts, J. (2)
  Milton, D. (2)
  Murray, B. (2)
  Sagan, C. (3)

Physics of Polar Phenomena

*Murray, B.
  Leighton, R. (1)
  Lederberg, J. (2)
  Leovy, C. (2)
  Sharp, R. (2)
  Soderblom, L. (2)
  Milton, D. (3)

Satellite Astronomy

*Pollock, J.
  Milton, D. (1)
  Davies, M. (2)
  Hartmann, W. (2)
  Sagan, C. (2)
  Veverka, J. (2)
  Smith, B. (3)
  Young, A. (4)

Variable Surface Features

*Sagan, C.
  Cutts, J. (1)
  Lederberg, J. (1)
  Levinthal, E. (1)
  Veverka, J. (1)
  Wildey, R. (1)
  Young, A. (1)
  Briggs, G. (2)
  Carr, M. (2)
  de Vaucouleurs, G. (2)
  Pollack, J. (2)
  Smith, B. (2)

---

*Principal investigator.

Note.—Number in parentheses indicates individual's choice in science discipline groups.

TASK GROUPS

Data Processing and Process Control

*Levinthal, E.
    Arthur, D.
    Batson, R.
    Briggs, G.
    Cutts, J.
    Davies, M.
    Shipley, E.
    Smith, B.
    Soderblom, L.
    Veverka, J.
    Wildey, R.
    Young, A.

Hardware

*Murray, B.
    Borgeson, W.
    Cutts, J.
    Leighton, R.
    Smith, B.
    Wildey, R.
    Young, A.

Mission Analysis

*Briggs, G.
    Borgeson, W.
    Davies, M.
    Milton, D.
    Pollack, J.
    Sagan, C.
    Smith, B.

Mission Operations

*Smith, B.
    Batson, R.
    Briggs, G.
    Carr, M.
    Hartmann, W.
    Leovy, C.
    McCauley, J.
    Murray, B.
    Sagan, C.

---

*Principal investigator.

Note.—Number in parentheses indicates individual's choice in science discipline groups.

APPENDIX C

Publications Resulting From Mariner 9

General: 30-Day Report, Science, vol. 175, Jan. 1972

STEINBACHER, R. H.; KLIORE, A.; LORELL, J.; HIPSHER, H.; BARTH, C. A.; MASURSKY, H.; MÜNCH, G.; PEARL, J.; AND SMITH, B.: Mariner 9 Science Experiments, Preliminary Results, p. 292.

MASURSKY, HAROLD; BATSON, R. M.; McCAULEY, J. F.; SODERBLOM, L. A.; WILDEY, R. L.; CARR, M. H.; MILTON, D. J.; WILHELMS, D. E.; SMITH, B. A.; KIRBY, T. B.; ROBINSON, J. C.; LEOVY, C. B.; BRIGGS, G. A.; YOUNG, A. T.; DUXBURY, T. C.; ACTON, C. H.; MURRAY, B. C.; CUTTS, J. A.; SHARP, R. P.; SMITH, SUSAN; LEIGHTON, R. B.; SAGAN, C.; VEVERKA, J.; NOLAND, M.; LEDERBERG, J.; LEVINTHAL, E.; POLLACK, J. B.; MOORE, J. T.; HARTMANN, W. K.; SHIPLEY, E. N.; DE VAUCOULEURS, G.; AND DAVIES, M. E.: Mariner 9 Television Reconnaissance of Mars and Its Satellites, Preliminary Results, p. 294.

HANEL, R. A.; CONRATH, B. J.; HOVAS, W. A.; KUNDE, V. G.; LOWMAN, P. D.; PEARL, J. C.; PRABHAKARA, C.; AND SCHLACHMAN, B.: Infrared Spectroscopy Experiment on the Mariner 9 Mission, Preliminary Results, p. 306.

CHASE, S. C.; HATZENBELER, H.; KIEFFER, H. H.; MINER, E.; MÜNCH, G.; AND NEUGEBAUER, G.: Infrared Radiometry Experiment on Mariner 9, p. 310.

BARTH, CHARLES A.; HORD, CHARLES W.; STEWART, A. IAN; AND LANE. ARTHUR L.: Mariner 9 Ultraviolet Spectrometer Experiment, Initial Results, p. 311.

KLIORE, A. J.; CAIN, D. L.; FJELDBO, G.; SEIDEL, B. L.; AND RASOOL, S. I.: Mariner 9 S-Band Martian Occultation Experiment, Initial Results on the Atmosphere and Topography of Mars, p. 315.

LORELL, J.; BORN, G. H.; CHRISTENSEN, E. J.; JORDAN, J. F.; LAING, P. A.; MARTIN, W. L.; SJOGREN, W. L.; SHAPIRO, I. I.; REASONBERG, R. D.; AND SLATER, G. L.: Mariner 9 Celestial Mechanics Experiment, Gravity Field and Pole Direction of Mars, p. 320.

LILLIE, CHARLES F.; BOHLIN, RALPH S.; MOLNAR, MICHAEL R.; BARTH, CHARLES A.; AND LANE, ARTHUR L.: Mariner 9 Ultraviolet Spectrometer Experiment, Stellar Observations, p. 324.

Selected topics from Icarus, vol. 17, Oct. 1972

McCAULEY, J. F.; CARR, M. H; CUTTS, J. A.; HARTMANN, W. K.; MASURSKY, H.; MILTON, D. J.; SHARP, R. P.; AND WILHELMS, D. E.: Preliminary Mariner 9 Report on the Geology of Mars, p. 289.

MURRAY, BRUCE C.; SODERBLOM, LAURENCE A.; CUTTS, JAMES A.; SHARP, ROBERT P.; MILTON, DANIEL L.; AND LEIGHTON, ROBERT B.: Geological Framework of the South Polar Region of Mars, p. 328.

SAGAN, CARL; VEVERKA, JOSEPH; FOX, PAUL; DUBISCH, RUSSELL; LEDERBERG, JOSHUA; LEVINTHAL, ELLIOTT; QUAM, LYNN; TUCKER, ROBERT; POLLACK, JAMES B.; AND SMITH, BRADFORD A.: Variable Features on Mars, Preliminary Mariner 9 Television Results, p. 346.

LEOVY, C. B.; BRIGGS, G. A.; YOUNG, A. T.; SMITH, B. A.; POLLACK, J. B.; SHIPLEY, E. N.; AND WILDEY, R. L.: The Martian Atmosphere, Mariner 9 Television Experiment Progress Report, p. 373.

POLLACK, J. B.; VEVERKA, J.; NOLAND, M.; SAGAN, CARL; HARTMANN, W. K.; DUXBURY, T. C.; BORN, G. H.; MILTON, D. J.; AND SMITH, B. A.: Mariner 9 Television Observations of Phobos and Deimos, p. 394.

HANEL, R.; CONRATH, B.; HOVIS, W.; KUNDE, V.; LOWMAN, P.; MAGUIRE, W.; PEARL, J.; PIRRAGLIA, J.; PRABHAKARA, C.; SCHLACHMAN, B.; LEVIN, G.; STRAAT, P.; AND BURKE, T.: Investigation of the Martian Environment by Infrared Spectroscopy on Mariner 9, p. 423.

HORD, C. W.; BARTH, C. A.; STEWART, A. I.; AND LANE, A. L.: Mariner 9 Ultraviolet Spectrometer Experiments, Photometry and Topography of Mars, p. 443.

BARTH, C. A.; STEWART, A. I.; HORD, C. W.; AND LANE, A. L.: Mariner 9 Ultraviolet Spectrometer Experiment, Mars Airglow Spectroscopy and Variations in Lyman Alpha, p. 457.

STEWART, A. I.; BARTH, C. A.; HORD, C. W.; AND LANE, A.

L.: Mariner 9 Ultraviolet Spectrometer Experiment, Structure of Mars' Upper Atmosphere, p. 469.

KLIORE, ARVYDAS J.; CAIN, DAN L.; FJELDBO, GUNNAR; SEIDEL, BORIS, L.; SYKES, MICHAEL J.; AND RASOOL, S. I.: The Atmosphere of Mars From Mariner 9 Radio Occultation Measurements, p. 484.

CAIN, D. L.; KLIORE, A. J.; SEIDEL, B. L.; AND SYKES, M. J.: The Shape of Mars From the Mariner 9 Occultations, p. 517.

Selected topics from Icarus, vol. 18, Jan. 1973

STEINBACHER, R. H.; AND HAYNES, N. R.: Mariner 9 Mission Profile and Project History, p. 64.

LANE, A. L.; BARTH, C. A.; HORD, C. W.; AND STEWART, A. I.: Mariner 9 Ultraviolet Spectrometer Experiment, Observations of Ozone on Mars, p. 102.

LEVINTHAL, E. C.; GREEN, W. B.; CUTTS, J. A.; JAHELKA, E. D.; JOHANSEN, R. A.; SANDER, M. J.; SEIDMAN, J. B.; YOUNG,

A. T.; AND SODERBLOM, L. A.: Mariner 9—Image Processing and Products, p. 75.

PANG, K. D.; AND HORD, C. W.: Mariner 9 Ultraviolet Spectrometer Experiment, 1971 Mars Dust Storm, p. 481.

LEOVY, C. B.: Exchange of Water Vapor Between the Atmosphere and Surface of Mars, p. 120.

Selected topics from Journal of Geophysical Research, vol. 78, July 10, 1973

MASURSKY, H.: Overview of the Geologic Results From Mariner 9, p. 4009.

CARR, M. H.; MASURSKY, H.; AND SAUNDERS, R. S.: A Generalized Geologic Map of Mars, p. 4031.

MILTON, D. J.: Water and Processes of Degradation in the Martian Landscape, p. 4037.

CARR, M. H.: Volcanism on Mars, p. 4049.

SHARP, R. P.: Mars, Troughed Terrain, p. 4063.

SHARP, R. P.: Mars, Fretted and Chaotic Terrains, p. 4073.

WILHELMS, D. E.: Comparison of Martian and Lunar Multi-Ringed Circular Basins, p. 4084.

HARTMANN, W. K.: Martian Cratering IV, Mariner 9 Initial Analysis, p. 4096.

SODERBLOM, L. A.; KREIDLER, T. J.; AND MASURSKY, H.: Latitudinal Distributions of Erosional Debris on the Martian Surface, p. 4117.

McCAULEY, J. F.: Mariner 9 Evidence for Wind Erosion in the Equatorial and Mid-Latitude Regions of Mars, p. 4123.

CUTTS, J. A.; AND SMITH, R. S. U.: Eolian Deposits and Dunes on Mars, p. 4139.

SAGAN, C.: Eolian Erosion on Mars, p. 4155.

SAGAN, C.; DUBISCH, R.; EROSS, B.; FOX, T.; FRENCH, R.; GIERASCH, P.; LEDERBERG, J.; LEVINTHAL, E.; POLLACK, J.; QUAM, L.; TUCKER, R.; AND VEVERKA, J.: Variable Features on Mars, Mariner 9 Global Results, p. 4163.

SODERBLOM, L. A.; MALIN, M. C.; CUTTS, J. A.; AND MURRAY,

B.: Mariner 9 Observations of the Surface of Mars in the North Polar Region, p. 4197.

CUTTS, J. A.: Wind Erosion in the Martian Polar Regions, p. 4211.

SHARP, R. P.: Mars, South Polar Pits and Etched Terrain, p. 4221.

CUTTS, J. A.: Nature and Origin of Layered Deposits of the Martian Polar Regions, p. 4231.

SAGAN, C.: Liquid Carbon Dioxide and the Martian Polar Laminae, p. 4250.

LEOVY, C. B.; BRIGGS, G. A.; AND SMITH, B. A.: Mars Atmosphere During the Extended Mission, Television Results, p. 4252.

CONRATH, B.; CURRAN, R.; HANEL, R.; KUNDE, V.; MAGUIRE, W.; PEARL, J.; PIRRAGLIA, J.; WELKER, J.; AND BURKE, T.: Atmospheric and Surface Properties of Mars Obtained by Infrared Spectroscopy on Mariner 9, p. 4267.

AJELLO, J. M.; HORD, C. W.; BARTH, C. A.; STEWART, A. I.; AND LANE, A. L.: Mariner 9 Ultraviolet Spectrometer Experiment, Afternoon Terminator Observation of Mars, p. 4279.

KIEFFER, H.; CHASE, S.; MINER, E.; MÜNCH, G.; AND NEUGEBAUER, G.: Preliminary Report on Infrared Radiometric Measurements From the Mariner 9 Spacecraft, p. 4291.

POLLACK, J.; VEVERKA, J.; NOLAND, M.; SAGAN, C.; DUXBURY, T.; ACTON, C.; BORN, G.; HARTMANN, W.; AND SMITH, B.:

Mariner 9 Television Observations of Phobos and Deimos, p. 4313.

LORELL, J.; AND SHAPIRO, I.: Mariner 9 Celestial Mechanics Experiment: A Status Report, p. 4327.

CALLAHAN, P.: Plasma Column Changes at Small Solar Elongations, p. 4330.

KLIORE, A.; FJELDBO, G.; SEIDEL, B.; SYKES, M. J.; AND WOICESHYN, P. M.: S-Band Radio Occultation Measurements of the Atmosphere and Topography of Mars With Mariner 9 —Extended Mission Coverage of Polar and Intermediate Latitudes, p. 4331.

CAIN, D.; KLIORE, A.; SEIDEL, B.; SYKES, M.; AND WOICESHYN, P.: Approximation to the Mean Surface of Mars and Mars Atmosphere Using Mariner 9 Occultations, p. 4352.

DAVIES, M. E.; AND ARTHUR, D. W. G.: Mariner 9 Control Net of Mars, p. 4355.

DE VAUCOULEURS, G.; DAVIES, M. E.; AND STURMS, F. M., JR.: The Mariner 9 Aerographic Coordinate System, p. 4395.

WU, S. S. C.; SCHAFER, F. J.; NAKATA, G. M.; JORDAN, R.; AND BLASIUS, K.: Photogrammetric Evaluation of Mariner 9 Photography, p. 4405.

BLASIUS, K.: Analytical Photogrammetry on Mars, p. 4411.

BATSON, R. M.: Cartographic Products From the Mariner 9 Mission, p. 4424.

DE VAUCOULEURS, G.; ROTH, J.; AND MULHOLLAND, C.: Albedo Map of South Polar Region, p. 4436.

Miscellaneous Papers

BARTH, C. A.; HORD, C. W.; STEWART, A. I.; LANE, A. L.; DICK, M. L.; AND ANDERSON, G. P.: Seasonal Variations of Ozone on Mars, Science, vol. 179, 1973, p. 795.

BECKER, R. A.: Mariner 9 TV Pictures Microfiche Library User's Guide, JPL Technical Memorandum TM-33-535, 1973.

CURRAN, R.; CONRATH, B.; HANEL, R.; KUNDE, V.; AND PEARL, J.: Mars: Mariner 9 Spectroscopic Evidence for H_2O Ice Clouds, Science, vol. 182, 1973, p. 381.

DE VAUCOULEURS, GERARD: Der rote Planet und Mariner 9, Bild der Wissenschaft, Autorensonderdruck, 1972, p. 1196.

DE VAUCOULEURS, GERARD: Telescopic Observations of Mars in 1971-I, Sky and Telescope, vol. 42, no. 5, Nov. 1971.

DE VAUCOULEURS, GERARD: Telescopic Observations of Mars in 1971-II, Sky and Telescope, vol. 42, no. 5, Nov. 1971.

DE VAUCOULEURS, GERARD: Telescopic Observations of Mars in 1971-III, Sky and Telescope, vol. 43, no. 1, Jan. 1972.

HAMMOND, ALLEN L.: The New Mars, Volcanism, Water, and a Debate Over Its History, Science, vol. 179, 1973, p. 463.

HARTMANN, W. K.: Martian Surface and Crust, Review and Synthesis, Icarus, vol. 19, 1973, p. 550.

HARTMANN, W. K., AND MARINER 9 TELEVISION EXPERIMENT TEAM: The New Mariner 9 Map of Mars, Sky and Telescope, vol. 44, 1972, p. 77.

KOSKELA, P.: Mariner Mars 1971 Television Picture Catalogue, JPL Technical Memorandum 33-585, Dec. 15, 1972.

LILLIE, C. F.; BOHLIN, R. C.; MOLNAR, M. R.; BARTH, C. A.; AND LANE, A. L.: Mariner 9 Ultraviolet Spectrometer Experiment, Stellar Observations, Science, vol. 175, 1973, p. 321.

MURRAY, B. C.; AND MALIN, M. C.: Polar Wandering on Mars, Science, vol. 179, 1973, p. 997.

MURRAY, B. C.; AND MALIN, M. C.: Polar Volatiles on Mars— Theory vs. Observation, Science, vol. 182, 1973, p. 437.

MURRAY, B. C.; WARD, W. R.; AND YEUNG, S. C.: Periodic Insulation Variations of Mars, Science, vol. 180, 1973, p. 638.

PHILLIPS, R. J.; SAUNDERS, R. S.; AND CONEL, J. F.: Mars, Crustal Structure Inferred From Bouger Gravity Anomalies, Journal of Geophysical Research, vol. 78, 1973, p. 4815.

SIEMENS, M.: Pogasis Users Guide, JPL Project Document 900-478, Nov. 1, 1971.

SNYDER, L. M.: Mariner 9 TV Subsystem Calibration Report, JPL Project Document 610-202, Nov. 15, 1972.

SODERBLOM, L. A.; AND WENNER, D. B.: A Fossil Water Table on Mars, submitted to Icarus.

STUART, J. R.: Mariner Mars 1971 Coordinate Systems, JPL Project Document 610-134, Aug. 10, 1970, Sept. 9, 1971.

THORPE, T. E.: Mariner 9 Star Photography, Applied Optics, Feb. 1973.

THORPE, T. E.: Mariner 9 Television Imaging Performance Evaluation, JPL Project Document 610-237, vol. II, Oct. 15, 1972.

THORPE, T.: Verification of the Mariner 9 Television Imaging Performance, submitted to the Journal of Spacecraft and Rockets.

VREBALOVICH, THOMAS: The Mariner 9 Orbiter Photographs of Mars, The Professional Photographer, vol. 99, no. 1922, July 1972.

WEIHAUPT, J.: Possible Origin and Probable Discharges of Meandering Channels on the Planet Mars, Journal of Geophysical Research, vol. 79, 1974, p. 2073.

Index

Note: Martian physical properties and topical charac-teristics are listed alphabetically, not under "Mars." Scientists serving in Mariner 9 team capacities are not referred to individually in the text or index.

☆ U. S. GOVERNMENT PRINTING OFFICE : 1974 O - 556- 083